Australian aborigine with sacred paintings at Ayers Rock, Central Australia

Photograph by C. P. Mountford

BRITISH MUSEUM (NATURAL HISTORY)

Races of Man

BY

SONIA COLE

P-21
P.B.

Second edition

LONDON

TRUSTEES OF THE BRITISH MUSEUM
(NATURAL HISTORY)

1965

Price Eleven Shillings and Sixpence net

First Edition 1963
Second Edition 1965
Reprinted 1968

Printed in England for HER MAJESTY'S STATIONERY OFFICE by
Butler & Tanner Ltd., Frome and London

Preface to Second Edition

The series of exhibits on the evolutionary history of Man, in the bays on the west side of the Central Hall, has been completed with a display in the fourth bay illustrating the Races of Man. This was prepared in 1958, and at the suggestion of Sir Gavin de Beer (then Director) the sixfold racial classification founded on blood-group gene frequencies as proposed by William C. Boyd was used as a working basis for the layout.

The exhibit was prepared in two months by Mrs. Caroline Banks, working with the staff of the Exhibition Section, in readiness for the commemoration of the Darwin-Wallace Centenary in July of that year.

There remained the need for a more considered treatment of the subject, and Mrs. Sonia Cole, already responsible for the preceding exhibit on the Neolithic Revolution, undertook to write this handbook on the Races of Man as a complement to the exhibit, and incidentally to R. Lydekker's 'Guide to the Specimens illustrating the Races of Mankind' (B.M.N.H., 4th edit., 1921), now long out of print. She has written it after consultation with many authorities, and as is inevitable with any work of synthesis in a controversial field, she has had to attempt to reconcile a number of conflicting views. Thanks are due to all those who so willingly gave their advice, particularly to Professor C. S. Coon, and to Professor Daryll Forde, Professor P. V. Tobias and Dr. J. S. Weiner.

In this second edition, some of the most significant advances in the field of human biology, particularly biochemistry, have been described (chapter IV).

Various authors, publishers and institutions have generously permitted the use of their photographs and figures in the preparation of this handbook, in particular the Shell International Petroleum Company Limited, and acknowledgment is made to them in the legends. The cover design and all the line drawings except Figs. 3, 4, 15, 19, 20, 26 and 27 were executed by Miss Rosemary Powers.

KENNETH OAKLEY
Deputy Keeper in charge,
(Sub-Department of Anthropology)

January, 1965

Contents

I

Definition of Race

The living races of the world are all members of one species, *Homo sapiens*, though there were probably at least one other genus and several species of man in the past. A species is defined as a group of actually or potentially interbreeding populations which, under natural conditions, does not interbreed with other species. Man is a polytypic species, that is one consisting of several sub-species and races. These different races arose through the isolation of groups by geographic or social barriers which prevented interbreeding with other groups. In the animal kingdom, the terms sub-species and race are often synonymous; or more often a race is a category lower than a sub-species. But in anthropology—the study of man—the term 'race' is often used very loosely.

To qualify as a sub-species, at least 75% of the individuals of a group must be taxonomically different from those of another group with which it is compared; this is known as the '75 per cent rule'. If we were to attempt to classify man according to this rule—which in fact is not done—we should be left with three sub-species: the Caucasoids (Whites or Europeans), the Mongoloids (Asians) and the Negroids (Blacks or Africans). Anthropologists often call these the primary or major stocks of mankind. There are also survivors of an ancient 'archaic White' or Palaeo-Asiatic stock which was probably widespread before the Caucasoids and the Mongoloids became differentiated. Survivors of this stock are grouped in the Australoid division of mankind, which includes the Australian aborigines. In addition, there are several secondary or composite stocks which, if they had remained isolated, would have become distinct sub-species: these are the American Indians and the Polynesians. The archaic White stock probably played a considerable part in the composition of the American Indians and the Polynesians; the first, however, are mainly Mongoloid, while the latter have less Mongoloid admixture.

Within these major groups of mankind there are a number of races and sub-races. A few of these have sometimes been called 'primary' for the sake of convenience—though obviously no true primary races still exist—while most are the result of admixture of 'primary' races and are known as 'composite'. An example

9

of a primary race is the Mediterranean Race of the Caucasoid stock; within this race there are a number of sub-races, in Europe, western Asia and India, North and north-eastern Africa.

Classifications such as these are useful in tracing broad relationships between the various groups. Without some such scheme a study of the living peoples of the world would be hopelessly confusing and a book like this would be unreadable. It must be emphasized, however, that racial divisions and sub-divisions are a matter of convenience and that classifications vary considerably according to the beliefs or prejudices of different authorities. Everywhere we find that human races and sub-races grade into one another, that there are 'clines' between neighbouring populations. The recent emphasis on human biology, particularly the study of blood groups and other biochemical characters (chapter IV), may eventually result in a really scientific appreciation of racial and individual variation, but these studies are still in their infancy.

The tremendous variations in individuals of any race or sub-race must be stressed, and although we may define the characteristics of a race as a whole, there will always be individuals of that race who do not conform to the general pattern. Some races are taller than average, others are shorter; but in every race there will be the tall and the short, the fat and the thin. Sheldon's classification of somatotypes is particularly useful in distinguishing between body-builds, which seem to be correlated with temperament, behaviour and susceptibility to certain diseases. A person's somatotype is rated by three sets of numerals from 1 to 7, expressing the degree of 'roundness' or endomorphy, muscularity or mesomorphy, and leanness or ectomorphy. Thus an extreme endomorph would be rated 7–1–1, an extreme mesomorph 1–7–1, and an extreme ectomorph 1–1–7 (most individuals, of course, have a moderate amount of each component).

Foundations of Classification

Linnaeus, in 1740, recognized four variants of man: European, American Indian, Asiatic and African. The first detailed scientific study of human races, however, was made by J. F. Blumenbach in 1775. He was the first to stress that the totality of all features must be taken into account in defining races and he recognized the extent to which differences grade into one another. Blumenbach's classification was based on skin colour, hair form and colour, eye colour, stature and measurements of various parts of the head and body. A vast number of records of measurements from both living populations and from skeletons have been collected from all over the world since the 18th century. Such data have been tabulated, analysed and interpreted. Statistics then show whether variations in populations are of racial significance.

One great advantage in using measurements is that they can be made on ancient bones as well as on living subjects and are therefore useful in tracing racial origins. Surface features such as skin colour and hair form, on the other hand, can be observed only on living people, except in rare cases when bodies have been preserved by mummification. Further, since they are purely metrical, measurements are not subject to observational uncertainties; providing they are accurate and are taken from agreed points, they must be purely objective. In the case of records of skin and hair colour made before the use of reflectometers, the visual judgement of the observer was involved and this subjective element lessened the value of such observations.

Most racial classifications have been founded on skeletal and surface features which together make up the phenotype or outward appearance of the individual. Until the science of genetics was developed early in the present century, physical anthropologists had no choice but to rely entirely on such characters in differentiating between races. Attempts have also been made to classify races according to the genotype, or genetic constitution of the individual; so far it has been possible to do this only for the major stocks and for a few races and sub-races with particular characteristics, but much progress in this direction may be expected in the future.

One of the main disadvantages in classification according to the phenotype is that the method of inheritance of most characters is not understood. Surface features are probably more strictly controlled by heredity than body shape and size, but both are influenced to a certain extent by environment, particularly by climate and diet. It is sometimes difficult to distinguish between permanent characters determined by heredity and therefore racially significant, and those which are temporary as the result of particular short-term environmental conditions. If such conditions persist over a long period, however, they will be reflected in the character of the race as a whole through the action of natural selection (p. 27).

As far as the three major stocks are concerned, there is generally little difficulty in placing individuals as Caucasoid, Mongoloid or Negroid on the basis of a few very obvious features such as skin colour, hair form and so on. In order to sub-divide these broad groups, however, more complicated combinations of characters must be assessed. No two individuals except identical twins are ever exactly alike owing to the enormous number of possible combinations of the genes inherited from both parents. The problem is to decide just which characters, and which of them in combination, are racially significant. Current research is very much concerned with the ways in which populations are affected both by heredity and environment and the *biological significance* of race differences.

Nationality has not necessarily any connection with race, nor has language or culture, though they have been responsible for isolating certain groups and thus indirectly affect gene frequencies. A race, in fact, differs from other races only in the frequency of the genes it possesses (chapter III); it is this that causes members of a race to look alike and, to some extent, to behave alike, though behaviour is also the result of a common culture.

Other Methods of Classification

Various attempts have been made to express by a single figure the degree of affinity or divergence between populations. These include the 'coefficient of racial likeness' (Pearson, 1921) and the 'generalized distance statistic' or D^2 (Mahalanobis, 1928). This distance statistic has been modified (Penrose, 1947, 1954) and split into two components of 'size' and 'shape'. These methods, which involve computation, are very useful to physical anthropologists but need not concern us further in this book.

Some anthropologists (Coon *et al.*, 1950) believe that if the four measurements of stature, weight, volume and surface area were available for large series of individuals of different races, they would provide mathematical constants which would go a long way towards establishing relationships. Although a start has been made in collecting such data, these measurements are not yet available on a world-wide scale. Coon and his co-authors therefore distinguish between races according to the following characteristics: evolutionary status as reflected in differences in teeth and jaws, skull thickness, size of brow-ridges and the presence or absence of 'archaic' features; body build as reflecting adaptations to extreme climatic conditions such as deserts, mountains or arctic temperatures; special surface features like black skin or flat faces which appear to be adaptations to different conditions of heat, light and cold.

Geneticists such as Boyd (1950) base schemes of classifications on differences in blood-group frequencies (chapter IV). Such a classification, based on characters which happen to have a simple mode of inheritance, is not necessarily the best one; it is *faute de mieux*. The blood groups, of course, have no distinguishing features visible to the eye and are not associated with any particular physical type of individual. But when large series of blood-group frequencies are examined, it is apparent that certain combinations of blood groups are characteristic of certain races. Blood-group evidence can also provide strong support for suspected racial relationships—perhaps based on culture or language—which cannot be proved by the older methods of physical anthropology.

It is generally agreed that the present distribution of the blood-group systems has been brought about by the same factors that have caused physical differences between populations: mixture, mutations, random variation and natural selection, particularly selection against certain diseases. In tracing racial origins the main difficulty is that parallel independent mutations may have produced identical effects in quite separate and genetically isolated populations. It is here that blood-group evidence can be most valuable in either supporting or contradicting conclusions based on the occurrence of similar physical features. Let us take as an example the Negroids of Africa and of Oceania (Melanesians and Papuans); do their black skins, frizzy hair, broad noses and so on imply a common origin; or are these features due to independent mutations which were maintained by natural selection in a similar environment? The great differences in their blood-group frequencies strongly suggest that independent mutations are the explanation and that there is no close relationship between the two peoples.

As Darwin (1871) remarked: 'It may be doubted whether any character can be named which is distinctive of race and is constant.' In the next three chapters we shall consider the most important characters of the phenotype and the genotype which cause racial differences, remembering that no clear-cut definition of human races has yet been made and that it is doubtful whether it ever can be made owing to the tremendous amount of mixing which has gone on and is still going on.

II

Physical Characters of Race

The main features used in defining human races are the following:

Skeletal features: the shape and size of the skull vault, face, nose, jaws and teeth; development of the brow-ridges; projection of the malars or cheek-bones; projection of the jaws (prognathism); stature and body build; proportions of the limbs and their segments.

Surface features: skin colour; hair form and colour; eye colour and eye-folds; form of the lips and extent to which they are everted; certain peculiarities, for instance an accumulation of fat on the thighs and buttocks (steatopygia), are also characteristic of some races. Modern research is revealing more and more variability in such details as finger-print patterns, distribution of body hair and so on.

Skeletal Features

In general, the following skeletal features are characteristic of the major divisions of mankind, Caucasoids, Negroids, Mongoloids and the less numerous but equally distinctive Australoids.

Caucasoids: Bones of the skeleton are heavier and thicker than in the case of the other stocks. Joints of long-bones are larger, muscular markings are more prominent. The pelvis is wider. The skull is characterized by more developed brow-ridges, large mastoid processes, a straight or orthognathous face, small jaws, high, narrow nasal bones and well-developed nasal spine, prominent chin.

Negroids: Slender long-bones; bones of forearm and shin long relative to bones of the upper segment of the limbs; narrow pelvis. Face marked by strong alveolar prognathism (bulging of the upper jaw in the sub-nasal region), poorly developed chin, low and broad nasal bridge, very broad nasal aperture, long and rather narrow palate and dental arch, rounded forehead, long or dolichocephalic skull, prominent occiput (back of the skull).

Mongoloids: There are no very distinctive features in the bones of the body;

14

it is the skull which is particularly diagnostic. Brachycephalic or round skull common; malars prominent and pushed forward so that the lower rim of the orbit (eye socket) is advanced; brow-ridges poorly developed; root of nose very flat and broad, bridge low, nasal aperture narrow; palate and dental arch short and wide; lower jaw wide with flaring hinder angles; shovel-shaped incisors (scooped out behind); flat occiput with marked torus or ridge; vault of the cranium often 'keeled' along its length.

Australoids: The Australoids have probably departed less from the form of early man than any of the other major stocks. Particularly characteristic are the receding forehead, prominent brow-ridges, and large palate and teeth. The body-build is slender, with long legs.

Certain measurements of the head, face, nose and body will now be considered in more detail.

The Head: Long-heads and Round-heads

Among the measurements which used to be considered particularly diagnostic was the cephalic index (on the living head) or the cranial index (when measurements are taken from the skull). The index is the breadth/length ratio expressed as a percentage. Skulls are classified as follows:

Dolichocephalic (long and narrow), cephalic index (referred to as c.i.) less than 75·9

Mesocephalic (medium), c.i. 76–80·9

Brachycephalic (short and broad), c.i. more than 81·0

It is usual to add **one** to two points to the cranial index to make it comparable with the cephalic index on the living head.

These terms to describe long-heads and round-heads were introduced by Huxley (1865) and skull measurements have been considered diagnostically very important ever since. On the whole, however, the cephalic index seems to be of limited significance as a criterion of race. Populations in Europe, Africa and Australia often have the same cranial index yet other features of the skull make them quite distinctive; but in distinguishing between groups within one major stock the cranial index often varies considerably and for this purpose it can be a useful measurement.

There are, of course, many other racially significant measurements of the

skull beside length and breadth; these include the height of the vault, breadth
and length of the face, occipital index, nasal index, form and shape of the orbits,
and so on. It is not enough to say that Nordics and Negroids have long, narrow
skulls, or that Alpines and Mongoloids have short, broad skulls; by themselves,
these features do not help very much, but all the differences taken together
make it possible to distinguish between such widely different peoples. Nordics,
for instance, have a narrow nasal opening, Negroids a wide one; Alpines have a
moderately wide nasal opening, Mongoloids a very narrow one.

Some of the characters of the skull are highly adaptive and are strongly
affected by climatic conditions, nutrition and other environmental factors. The
nasal index, for example, is certainly affected by temperature (p. 18). Whether
the actual shape of the skull is influenced by environment has not been proved,
though there is some evidence that Hawaiian-born Japanese have rounder heads
than their immigrant parents.

It is possible sometimes to guess a person's race from the shape of his skull—
for instance the low-vaulted skull of the Australian aborigine with his large
brow-ridges, or the jutting malars and 'keeled' cranium of the Eskimo are un-
mistakable—but more often than not the race of an individual cannot be determined from the skull alone.

During the early stages of man's evolution, the shape of the skull was strongly
affected by the attachments of powerful neck and jaw muscles. These needed
reinforcements in the form of a torus or ridge at the back of the skull or in the
form of brow-ridges respectively. The strongly developed brow-ridges of Java
Man or Neanderthal Man are one of the most striking features of these skulls. As
the brain grew in size, the jaws remained constant or shrank and the need for
strong muscle attachment was less. The shape of the skull now depends more on
its contents than on mechanical duties; an exception is the Eskimo, whose jaws
have to chew not only tough meat but also skins in order to soften them and this
has strongly affected the shape of his high 'keeled' cranium.

In Upper Palaeolithic times, skulls were typically dolichocephalic. Brachycephalic skulls appeared only very occasionally before Mesolithic times, when they
became relatively common. At Ofnet in Bavaria, for instance, 8 out of 21 skulls
of Mesolithic age were brachycephalic. Most of the Neolithic immigrants to
Europe were long-headed, but during the Bronze Age there were extensive
movements of predominantly round-headed people from Asia Minor, central
Europe and Spain. In Great Britain, the predominantly long-headed Neolithic

population was also replaced by round-heads during the Bronze Age. There was again an increase in dolichocephaly during the Early Iron Age and Roman periods, after which round-heads became common once more. In historic times, there has been a general tendency for skulls to become rounder, particularly in central and eastern Europe where this trend has been attributed to successive invasions of round-headed Mongoloids, the Huns, Avars, Turks, Tatars and Mongols. The general increase of round-heads must presumably be the result of natural selection, though the advantages are obscure. Huizinga (1958) concluded that brachycephalization may be the result of a kind of arrested development. The position of the point of greatest breadth, attained at the age of 9 months, shifts with age; after 9 months, the skull undergoes a phase of secondary long-headedness. Huizinga considers that the present 'infantile' trend towards round-headedness will in the future develop in the direction of a secondary phase of long-headedness, rather than towards increasing brachycephalization.

The Face

The facial index is less useful than the cephalic index as a racial criterion in living populations as it is affected by function, as well as by age and sex. Men usually have longer faces than women of the same race because their jaws are heavier and deeper, the upper lip is longer and the chin is more powerful. Strong-jawed people usually have broad faces, as well as long ones. Long faces may also be associated with an over-active pituitary gland, while short, broad faces are sometimes due to thyroid deficiency.

The facial index is the length of the face from the root of the nose to the bottom of the chin, expressed as a percentage of the greatest breadth across the cheek-bones. Facial indices on the living head are as follows:

> Broad—less than 85
> Medium—85–88
> Narrow—more than 88

Mongoloids have the broadest faces, Caucasoids the narrowest. Negroids are characterized more particularly by prognathism, a protrusion of the jaws which causes the whole face to jut forward; this condition is also found typically in the Australoids, in many types of early man, and also in the great apes. A straight or orthognathous face is most marked in Caucasoids.

B

The Nose

The nasal index is the percentage ratio of breadth to height; on the skull, nasal classification is as follows:

> Leptorrhine (narrow), nasal index less than 47·9
> Mesorrhine (medium), nasal index 48–52·9
> Platyrrhine (broad), nasal index more than 53.

On the living subject, the nasal index is higher; it varies from less than 70 (leptorrhine) to more than 84 (platyrrhine). Noses of females tend to be broader and shorter than those of males and the nasal index decreases considerably with age. Australoids are the most platyrrhine of the living races and Negroids too have short, broad noses; most Mongoloids are mesorrhine, except for the Eskimos who, like the Caucasoids, are typically leptorrhine.

The shape of the nasal aperture may be strongly affected by climate. In hot, moist climates, the nasal aperture is generally broad; in cold, dry climates it is narrow. Temperature is more important than humidity. A restricted air intake under cold conditions would seem to be essential to lessen the danger of chilling the lungs; but Washburn (1963) considers that there is no evidence that nose form is affected by the necessity of warming the air intake.

The nose itself, of course, may be of many different shapes. The profile, which includes the root, bridge, tip and septum separating the nostrils, may be concave, straight or convex and there are various forms within each of these categories. The wings of the nostrils and the shape of the nostrils also vary considerably. Certain general types are racially typical. The Negro nose is short and has a broad, depressed root; the bridge is also broad and may be concave or straight; the tip is thick and usually turned upwards; the wings are thick and flaring, the nostrils round. The Australoid nose is similar, but the root is more deeply depressed, the tip larger, and the wings even more spreading. The Mongoloid nose is strongly concave and 'infantile'; compared with the Negroid nose it has a lower and less broad root, a lower and narrower bridge, a less bulbous tip, thinner wings and septum. Caucasoids, particularly Nordics and Mediterraneans, are characterized by a nose that is often convex and typically narrow, with high root and bridge, long tip, and depressed wings. The Alpines of central Europe have a shorter, broader nose, often straight in profile, with a rather thick tip. The hooked Armenoid or 'Jewish' nose is seen also among Melanesians and Papuans. American

Indians, particularly the Plains Indians, often have a convex bridge, a tip prolonged downward, and very flaring wings.

Stature

The effects of climate on stature and body build are discussed on pp. 30–31. In general, light-weight, lean people live in the hotter parts of the world, particularly in deserts, while the short, thick-set people live in cold climates. Owing to

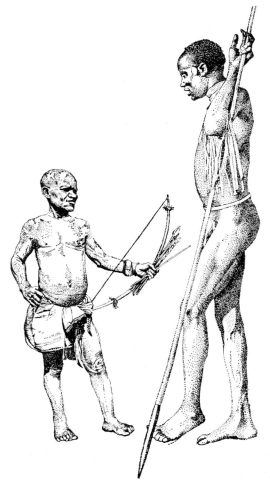

Fig. 1. The shortest and the tallest people in the world—Congo pygmies and Nilotic Negroes such as the Dinka—both live in tropical Africa.

Based on photographs by Shell and Bernatzik

mixture and migrations, however, there are many exceptions to this generalization. Stature is mainly hereditary and differences in size cannot be explained wholly by environmental factors, whether climate, diet or occupation—although these conditions may sometimes modify stature, for instance in times of famine. Pygmies (Fig. 1; Plate VIII) may well be modified representatives of the local populace, living under conditions of isolation, who acquired their physical distinction by inbreeding in an adverse environment. Lesser degrees of the same trend are found among Bushmen, Eskimos and Lapps.

According to their stature, men are grouped as follows (women average about 20 cm. shorter in each case):

> Very short or pygmy, less than 149·9 cm. (5 ft.)
> Short, 150–159·9 cm. (5 ft.–5 ft. 4 in.)
> Medium, 160–169·9 cm. (5 ft. 4 in.–5 ft. 8 in.)
> Tall, 170–179·9 cm. (5 ft. 8 in.–6 ft.)
> Very tall, more than 180 cm. (6 ft.)

Allowing for the great individual variation found in all groups, stature is still racially characteristic in many instances:

Very short: Negrito (Asiatic and Oceanic) and Negrillo (African) pygmies; Bushmen.

Short: Indonesians; Ainu; Eskimo; Lapps; Yahgan and Carib American Indians.

Medium: Most Caucasoid, Mongoloid and Negroid groups; Australoids; American Indians along Pacific coast of both Americas.

Tall: Tallness is commoner in Africa than in any other continent, particularly in the Eastern Lake region (Nilotic Negroids); N.W. Europeans and Dinarics; North Chinese; Plains Indians and certain groups in south-west U.S.A. and Patagonia; Polynesians; Melanesians and Papuans.

Surface Features

In distinguishing between the major stocks, the most obvious differences are those of skin colour; hair colour and form; and eye colour. These differences, however, are not generally useful in the classification of races of the same stock since they grade into one another.

Skin Colour

Conditions of light and heat, particularly light, under varying degrees of humidity have a considerable effect on skin colour (see p. 30). But the skin colours of the major groups or stocks are distinctive in a way which defies the easy explanation of climatic adaptation as the sole cause.

Anthropologists compare skin colour by means of the spectrophotometer. Using light filters representing regions of the spectrum, the amount of light reflected back from the skin surface is recorded for a series of individuals. From such data, graphs can be drawn from which it is possible to compare accurately the skin colour for different groups.

Individuals vary greatly in the concentration of pigment, mostly a form of melanin, in the epidermis. The amount of melanin is inherited, but a number of genes are involved and the exact mode of inheritance is not known. The difference in skin colour between Negroes and Whites is believed to be caused by more than three pairs of genes; it is probable that some pigment genes are scattered in white populations and some genes for lightness of the skin in Negro populations (Dobzhansky, 1955). Although there is some evidence to show that the production of melanin is influenced by hormones of the adrenal cortex, there is nevertheless a direct relation between intensity of ultra-violet light radiation and the intensity of pigmentation.

Dark skins absorb more visible radiation than light skins—80% or more, compared with about 60% in white skins. The invisible heat rays at the infra-red end of the spectrum are absorbed almost equally by blacks and whites. But the invisible ultra-violet rays from the other end of the spectrum penetrate a white skin deeply, whereas the pigmented layer in a black skin acts as a filter so that far less ultra-violet light gets through. Under conditions of strong sunlight, enough ultra-violet penetrates to be used in the production of the necessary amount of vitamin D. But it has been found that Negro children under cloudy skies are more susceptible to rickets than white children and this has been attributed to the filter action of the melanin in their skins.

Desert dwellers living in areas of very strong sunlight often have brown rather than black skins, but here it seems that aridity is an important factor (see Gloger's rule, p. 30). The Tasmanians were very dark although they lived in a temperate climate; but they were comparatively recent immigrants to Tasmania and certainly originated nearer the Equator. There are no indigenous people with black skins in the New World; it has been suggested that the genes for black skins were 'eliminated' when their ancestors passed through the 'cold filter' after crossing the Bering Straits and no subsequent mutations for this character have arisen since the American Indians became isolated. Since there is no evidence of genes for black skins having been present in their Mongoloid ancestors, however, perhaps 'eliminated' is not the right word.

It seems most likely that early man had a brownish skin and that mutations took place both in the direction of lighter and darker skins. Mutations involving increased pigmentation would be advantageous in the tropics and were therefore encouraged by natural selection. Mutations towards blondness would seem to offer an advantage in relation to vitamin D formation in higher latitudes, sunlight being absorbed more readily through lighter skins.

Hair Form and Colour

Hair has been classified as follows:

> Leiotrichous (straight, as in the Mongoloids)
> Cynotrichous (straight, wavy or curly, as in Caucasoids)
> Helicotrichous (helical, or spiral, as in Negroids)

Tightly curled hair occurs in two forms—helical, in which the loops are of constant diameter, and spiral, in which the loops diminish in diameter outwards from the scalp. The extreme form of spiral hair is known as 'peppercorn', in which there are open spaces between the clusters of hair.

The greatest centre of helical hair is in Africa, with another centre in Melanesia and with islands of spiral-haired Negritos in between. Helical hair, as seen for instance in Sudanese Negroes and Melanesians, grows in a tight mat and might have a protective value in areas of strong sunlight where there is little shade. The centres of spiral hair follow the belt of tropical rain forests, a belt which was probably wider at various times in the past. This form of hair seems to be of ancient origin and has spread further afield than its companion black skin.

Peppercorn hair might be an advantage in the hot, damp conditions of forests since the open spaces between the clusters of hair would allow sweat from the scalp to evaporate. Peppercorn hair is typical of Bushmen, who now live in the desert; but they undoubtedly had a wider distribution in the past and may have had a common origin with the pygmies, who also have peppercorn hair but to a lesser extent. This peculiar form of hair is also found among the Andaman Islanders.

Helical and spiral hair might have spread from a single centre; more probably it arose in different parts of the tropical belt by parallel mutations. Outside Africa, spiral hair occurs among pygmies in the forests of Malaya, Sumatra, New Guinea and the Philippines as well as among the tall Papuans and Melanesians.

Hair form is apparently controlled by a large number of genes, which makes it probable that a great many mutations have occurred. In Negro-White crosses, the Negroid traits of skin colour and hair form are apparently inherited independently. Straight, coarse Mongoloid hair seems to be dominant over woolly hair, while fine, straight Caucasoid hair is recessive. Although there is probably an advantage in woolly hair as a protection for the scalp in strong sunlight, and to a certain extent curly hair would also be advantageous in this way, there seem to be no obvious advantages or disadvantages in straight or wavy hair.

Hair colour depends on the black or brown granular pigment identical with that in the skin. In albinos this pigment is absent. In the case of blond hair the pigment is usually confined to the middle layer or cortex of the hair shaft; but in black hair the inner part or medulla is also full of melanin. In addition to melanin, a red acid-soluble pigment known as trichosiderin is sometimes present (Barnicot, 1956). The mechanism of inheritance of red hair is probably genetically simple, while the inheritance of other kinds of pigmentation of hair seems to be complicated.

Hair colour cannot be explained on climatic grounds as easily as skin colour. Although blondness is mainly confined to northern Europe and to migrants from this area, the Monogoloids of the coldest parts of Siberia or Greenland have hair as black as those living in the tropics.

Development of beard and body hair also varies considerably among the races, It is strongest among 'archaic Whites' such as the Australian aborigines and Ainu. as well as among the Caucasoids, and is least developed among Negroids and Mongoloids.

Eye Colour and Form

Eyes are classified as light, mixed, brown or black. Blue (light) eyes are generally recessive to brown, the commonest colour. Eye colour sometimes darkens with age and there seems to be some sexual difference: women tend to have darker eyes than men of the same race and age.

The black Negro eye is due to the density of pigment in the outer layer of the iris, while the brown eye colour of lighter-skinned races is mainly due to pigment in the middle layer showing through the unpigmented outer layer. In blue eyes, pigment is found only in the lower layer of the iris; it appears blue when seen through the muscles of the upper layers. It seems that the heavily pigmented eyes of Negroids, and the less heavily pigmented eyes of Mongoloids, are genetically distinct from dark brown Caucasoid eyes.

The black superficial iris pigment of the Negroid probably serves to reinforce the pigmented layer on the back of the iris against the penetration of ultra-violet light. In strong light, the dark granules in the basal layer screen the bases of the light-sensitive cells. Albinos, and to a lesser extent people with blue eyes, have difficulty in resolving images on a bright day because the visible light enters through the iris tissue in addition to that which goes through the pupil. Dark-eyed people have a higher resolving power under intense illumination and this must have been very important for hunters, who must be able to distinguish game from afar. Possibly brown eyes are of more ancient origin and light ones arose through mutations, persisting in areas where there was little or no selective disadvantage against them.

There are only two forms of eye: Mongoloid and non-Mongoloid. The latter is more deeply recessed in its socket and in the former the external angle of the eyelid opening is often higher than the internal angle. The most striking feature of the Mongoloid eye is the fold of the upper lid, which may run the whole length of the lid or may be restricted to the inner corner, when it is known as the internal epicanthus or epicanthic fold. This feature seems to be dominant in crosses between Mongoloids and other races. The epicanthic fold is also common among Bushmen, where it presumably arose as an independent parallel mutation. It has been suggested that the eye-fold and yellow-skin of the Bushmen indicate crossing with Mongoloids; but the fact that the dominant Mongoloid hair form never appears among Bushmen would be enough to discount this theory apart from the blood-group evidence (p. 34).

The epicanthic fold in Bushmen may be a protection against sun glare. In Mongoloids, it may be a secondary effect produced by modification of the face in response to cold during the last glaciation. To reduce the protrusion of the nose—which would otherwise be frozen—the cheek bones moved forward and enlarged; as they moved, so did the eyeballs, which became protected from freezing by fatty layers padding the lids. The slit so formed also protects the eye against snow glare.

Other Surface Features

A number of other surface features are racially distinctive, many of them with no obvious advantage. These include thickened tissues, such as the thick, everted Negroid lip. African Negroes and Melanesians are the only two groups with black skins, woolly hair and thick lips; yet their blood-group frequencies are so different that it seems unlikely that they had a common origin. These three characters may well have arisen by independent parallel muta-

tions and, so far as black skins and woolly hair are concerned, were probably maintained through natural selection in tropical environments. The coincidence of both groups developing everted lips is less easy to explain. Caucasoids have the thinnest lips, while Mongoloids are intermediate in this respect.

Ears also show racial differences. Negroids have a short, wide ear with little or no lobe while Bushmen and Hottentots have a very distinctive ear—it is short and broad with a deep roll of the helix or rim and the lobe is very small or absent. Caucasoids generally have fairly long, narrow ears; Australoids and Mongoloids have the longest and narrowest ears of all.

Other variable features with no apparent advantages include dermatoglyphic patterns. Statistical trends in the incidence of ridge patterns (arches, whorls and loops) on fingers, palms, soles and toes show some racial variability.

One of the distinctive racial features which is probably advantageous is the thick layer of fat

Fig. 2. A woman of the Andaman Islands showing steatopygia, characteristic also of the Bushwomen of S. Africa (see Plate X).

Based on a photograph by Ciprian

on thighs and buttocks of Bushwomen, known as steatopygia. This may act as a food- or water-store in times of famine and the fact that it is developed more in women than men suggests that this consideration may be particularly important in pregnancy. Steatopygia is sometimes found in the Congo pygmies, but is far commoner among Bushmen and Hottentots (Plate X). It is also found among Andaman Island pygmies (Fig. 2).

III

Genetics and Evolution

Geneticists believe that racial categories must be based on the genetic constitution or genotype, rather than on the outward appearance, or phenotype. The genotype is determined entirely by heredity and is fixed at conception; its inherent potentialities, however, may result in different phenotypes, which change throughout the life of an individual and vary according to the environment.

Unfortunately, most of the outward characters which distinguish one race from another are controlled by a large number of genes—the units of heredity—and their mode of inheritance has not yet been worked out. A few characters, notably the blood groups, are determined by only a few genes—sometimes only by one—and it is for this reason that they have proved so valuable in tracing origins and relationships.

Principles of Genetics

The study of genetics originated with Mendel's discovery of the mechanism of inheritance, a work which remained unnoticed for 40 years until it was rediscovered at the beginning of the present century.

The unit of heredity, the gene, is a complex nucleo-protein. The genes are part of the chromosomes, which are rod-like structures in the nucleus of the cells, composed of nucleoproteins and deoxyribosenucleic acids, generally known as DNA. Each member of a gene pair is known as an allele, the two genes having been inherited one from each of the parents. Alleles may be composed of two dominant genes, expressed with capital letters (AA), or recessive genes, expressed with small letters (aa). In these two cases the individual would be homozygous for the character concerned. The offspring of homozygous parents, however, might inherit the dominant gene A from one and the recessive gene a from another; in this case, he would be heterozygous for that character, Aa.

Man has 23 pairs of chromosomes and the number of possible combinations is 2^{23}, or more than 16 million. In practice, an individual is believed to be the product of about 44,000 pairs of genes. Of these, some 90% are held in common by everyone.

Of the remaining 5,000 or so, at least half must be allowed for sexual differences and racial variations and only about 2,500 genes—3–5% of the whole—remain to account for individual variations.

Genetics and Evolution

Evolution is essentially a change in gene frequencies resulting from the production of new genes, the loss of genes, or an accumulation of changes in gene frequencies. Frequencies may be altered by *mixture* of populations, *mutations*, *natural selection*, and *genetic drift* or random variation. Races converge by mixture and diverge through natural selection, isolation and genetic drift.

The most important agency in bringing about changes in gene frequencies of human populations is *mixture*; at the present time, this is going on to such an unprecedented extent that it is bound to lead to a merging of the races we know. Perhaps the strongest isolating mechanism holding this process in check is 'assortative mating' caused by class, social and other artificial barriers; but as a result of better education, the general trend nowadays is towards a breakdown of these barriers.

A *mutation* is the appearance of a new hereditary character that breeds true. Mutations arise from changes in the chemical composition of the gene or of the chromosome which alter its inherent potentialities. Most organisms are in such good equilibrium with their environment as a result of natural selection that any change is likely to be for the worse. Mutations, however, provide the raw material for evolution; from this material, natural selection determines which of the many potential characters shall survive. It is this interaction of mutations and natural selection which gives rise to evolutionary change.

It has been shown mathematically that a very small selective advantage can lead to the rapid spread of new genes in a population. *Natural selection* operates most strongly under rigorous environmental conditions, or where there is much competition; under such conditions, only the most efficient forms will survive. Where there is little 'selective pressure', on the other hand, there is scope for many different varieties. In the history of man over the past few thousand years, disease has undoubtedly had a very important selective effect. During the food-gathering stage—99% of human history—the population was so small and scattered that diseases probably did not spread; but after the beginnings of village and city life and before advances in hygiene were made, those with no inherited immunity to diseases were rapidly eliminated. It is estimated that nearly a quarter of the population of Europe died from the Black Death in the 14th century; the outcome of such an epidemic must result in a significant change in the genetic composition of the population. Recent studies have shown that natural selection against disease, particularly malaria, has been responsible for the frequencies of certain blood groups, abnormal haemoglobins and other biochemical characters (chapter IV).

In small, isolated populations, evolutionary changes may for a time appear to proceed against the direction of natural selection through the effect of *genetic drift* or random variation. This was first observed by Sewall Wright and is sometimes known as the Sewall Wright effect. When a small population is isolated, it may lose some of its genes altogether through the failure to breed of the few individuals possessing those particular genes. Quite by chance, advantageous genes may be lost and non-adaptive or 'disadvantageous' ones become fixed. In this way also differences in traits which seem adaptively neutral may arise between populations.

It will be seen that individuals in different parts of the world sharing certain features in common need not necessarily have inherited these genes from a common ancestor. Independent parallel mutations may, and almost certainly do, occur. This makes the task of the investigator of racial origins extremely complicated.

The Influence of Environment

The influence of environment on evolutionary changes is very important. Geography affects human populations directly—by isolation resulting from barriers such as mountain ranges, deserts, oceans and so on—and indirectly through the effects of climate and diet. Cultural barriers, such as the isolating factors of language, religion and rank or caste, are often nearly as significant as physical barriers.

Geographic Barriers

New sub-species or races are most commonly formed through the divergence of populations separated from one another by geographic barriers. In the animal world this is not the only method of species formation—groups might become differentiated by becoming specialized to a particular diet or to combat new enemies or diseases—but it is certainly the most important one. Barriers prevent interbreeding and encourage genetic drift; moreover, the environment on either side of a mountain range or a desert is likely to be different and natural selection may operate in different ways in each area. The Sahara, for instance, separates the Mediterranean Caucasoids from the Negroids of tropical Africa; the Himalayas divide Mongoloids of the high plateaus of central Asia from the Indian Caucasoids living in the hot, moist, low-lying plains. Geographic barriers have always been less effective against the movements of man than of other animals owing to man's great adaptability. His omnivorous diet and his mastery over tools and fire enabled him to survive under the most varied conditions. The one effective barrier in ancient times was the ocean, which guarded the New World until a land bridge connected it with Asia towards the end of the Ice Age; the ocean also prevented settlement of the Pacific islands until a few thousand years ago after efficient boats had been invented.

The main ways in which geographic barriers may affect evolutionary trends are the following:

(1) by keeping out new genes which would otherwise come from other populations;

(2) by relaxing the selection pressure, since there is less competition in a restricted environment;

(3) by aiding genetic drift;

(4) by being the cause of special climatic or nutritional conditions favouring different types.

The effects of isolation of small populations are well known from Darwin's observations on the Galapagos islands. Mutations arising in other restricted environments have produced dwarf elephants and hippopotamuses on Mediterranean islands during the Pleistocene. The classic example of survival of archaic forms in regions where there is no competition is the marsupial fauna of Australia. In the case of human populations, the effects of isolation are less obvious but they do in fact occur. The emergence of the Mongoloid type is thought to have taken place in isolated areas surrounded by ice during the last glaciation. This is an example of 'dynamic' natural selection, involving the establishment of a new genotype adapted to the rigorous conditions of a changed environment. 'Stabilizing' natural selection, on the other hand, favours types able to withstand change—such as extreme seasonal ranges of temperature or times of famine—but it does not encourage the formation of new genotypes.

The Effects of Climate

Through natural selection, the effects of climate may encourage some characters and discourage others. In cold climates, adaptations are favoured which minimize heat loss; in hot climates, those which facilitate body cooling are favoured. Such adaptations take place in response to both latitude and altitude.

Adaptation to climate in animals in general is governed by three rules. Gloger's rule states that pigmentation is greatest in warm and humid areas. The association of black skins with heat applies broadly in the case of man; the fact that desert dwellers have brown rather than black skins can be accounted for by the absence of humidity. In the dry atmosphere of the tropical deserts evaporation takes place readily, so that there is less discomfort than in a damp atmosphere. Also, in many cases the lighter-skinned desert people are comparatively recent arrivals; the Tuareg, for instance, have probably lived in the Sahara for only about 1,500 years. In some areas of extreme cold, brown skins are also found. It has been suggested that the Eskimo are such relatively recent arrivals that they have not had enough time to lose their pigmentation; to some extent, also, their brown skins may serve as a protection against sun glare. There is no reason to suppose that brown skin is *dis*advantageous in cold areas (as it would be in the case of animals needing camouflage in the snow, thus encouraging selection for white fur or feathers), so there is no apparent reason why it should be eliminated by selection.

Bergman's rule states that animals are smaller in warmer than in cooler climates. This does not apply to stature so much as body build. In human populations, both the shortest—pygmies—and the tallest—Nuer, Dinka, Tutsi—people on earth live near the equator, but their build is slender. All people living round the Arctic circle are short, but they are thick-set with broad chests and padded with fat. They present the least possible surface in proportion to their volume and weight and are built to radiate as little heat as possible.

The third of these rules, Allen's rule, states that the extremities of the body are shorter in cold climates; the extremities include limbs, ears, nose, and tail in the case of animals. The Eskimos have very short legs, toes, fingers and noses. Desert dwellers, on the other hand, have long slender limbs and often prominent noses (which would soon get frozen in Siberia or Greenland).

The skin surface area of desert dwellers is great in proportion to volume and weight, thus presenting a maximum of cooling surface for evaporation. In the case of people living in moist heat, however, an increase in surface area by means of long limbs would not cause heat loss because of the difficulty of evaporation in a saturated atmosphere. Thus we find that the pygmies, Indonesians, and American Indians of the Amazon basin do not have the lanky form of desert dwellers.

Of the special adaptations to climate, none is so striking as those for conditions of dry cold. The people who live in the coldest part of the earth are the Tungus of eastern Siberia, where a temperature of $-96°$ F. has been recorded. They are the most extreme Mongoloids, with short, thick-set bodies, flat faces, fat-lidded eyes, coarse black hair and scanty beard and body hair. These features probably developed in response to the extreme cold of the last glacial period, the peak of which was about 25,000 years ago. The people of northern Europe and northern Asia then lived in isolated communities surrounded by ice and either they became adjusted or became extinct. Such conditions were ideal for adaptive changes of an extreme kind. The face became moulded by 'climatic engineering' (Coon et al., 1950). Protuberances were flattened to reduce the surface area to a minimum (Fig. 3; Plate IV) and the face was padded with fat to prevent loss of heat. Beardlessness, too, may have some selective value since moisture from the breath would freeze on the beard and so freeze the face underneath.

The adaptations of the Mongoloids provide an excellent example of the rapid alteration of gene frequencies in response to natural selection. Where conditions are rigorous, however, advantageous mutations have a high selective value. It has been suggested (Washburn, 1963) that the Mongoloid face is the result not so much of climate but of the large masseter muscles used in chewing tough food, with consequent enlargement of the bones to which these muscles are attached.

The fossil evidence suggests that man evolved in the warmer parts of the world and moved to colder areas only after he had acquired fire and clothing. He was thus able to survive outside his original environment and was subjected to greater variations of climate than any other mammal. Yet, unlike other animals with very varied habitats, man has not differentiated into more than one species. The explanation is not only that man is extremely mobile and has interbred widely, but more important, that he has a relatively unspecialized body not adapted exclusively for any particular environment. This lack of specialization must be attributed to culture; man's mastery over tools and weapons has made major skeletal adaptations unnecessary.

Fig. 3. The flat Mongoloid face may be a cold adapted feature (or perhaps the result of diet) which increased through natural selection during the Last Glacial Period.

After Dobzhansky, 'Evolution, Genetics and Man' (John Wiley)

Although the races of the world differ so much in appearance owing to adaptations to their environment, all are able to survive in almost any climate because of the artificial aids at man's disposal: shelter, clothing, prepared foods and so on. The physiological effects of living in a foreign environment are less important than the psychological, which may call for far more adjustment.

The Effects of Diet

The effects of diet on the morphology of organisms of all kinds are generally profound. Meat-eaters are usually big, such as the Palaeolithic mammoth hunters or the Plains Indians who lived on bison. Their lives called for maximum strength and endurance and their bones were large in proportion. At the other extreme are the small people of south-eastern Asia whose diet is almost exclusively polished rice. On a similar diet, Europeans would soon develop beri beri and other deficiency diseases, but the indigenous people have become adapted to the minimum essentials for maintaining life through many generations during which natural selection has favoured the small. There is evidence to show that these people grow larger on a 'western' diet in the U.S.A. or in Hawaii.

In Polynesia and Micronesia many of the people are as tall and heavy as western Europeans and Americans, although they eat practically no meat. Their diet includes sweet potatoes, yams, taro, coconuts and fish. The roots, however, are rich in certain essential amino acids, while the sea food protein also contains numerous amino acids, calcium and other necessary minerals.

Desert dwellers live on a concentrated low-bulk, high-protein, high-fat and high-sugar diet which includes milk, dates and some grains. They eat no bulky high-cellulose vegetables, which do not grow in deserts. A lean, short-gutted body requires more concentrated food, while a long-gutted bulky body can tolerate high-bulk low-concentrate diets (Coon, 1957).

Arctic peoples need enormous quantities of fatty foods because much of the fat they eat is expended in heat loss. They have almost twice the caloric requirements of people of the tropical zones. The effects of chewing tough food, reflected in the size and form of muscles, teeth and the bony structure of the face, are marked in the case of some of the Mongoloids, particularly the Eskimos (pp. 31, 96) and are very noticeable in the skulls of early men and of the Australian aborigines.

c

IV

Blood Groups and other Biochemical Characters

Of all the inherited characters, only the blood groups have been studied in detail on a world-wide basis. This is not only because their method of inheritance is so simple, but also because of their importance in medicine; since it was discovered that blood transfusions were effective only if blood of the right group was used, patients and donors have been 'typed' and data on blood groups now exist for millions of people from all parts of the world.

The A B O Groups

In the first years of the present century, Landsteiner discovered that human bloods could be tested to show four different groups: A, B, AB and O. During the first world war, it was found that the frequencies of these groups varied considerably in different populations. Since the A B O groups were distinguished and their genetics worked out in 1924, at least 10 other genetically independent systems have been found.

The A B O groups are determined by the presence of a mucopolysaccharide (the antigen) on the red corpuscles of the blood. When red cells are mixed with the fluid part of the blood (serum) from an individual of a different group, the red cells become stuck together or agglutinated owing to the action of ABO antibodies in the serum.

The mechanism of inheritance depends on three alleles and in theory six combinations are possible, producing six genotypes: AA, BB, AB, AO, BO, OO. But since O can only be distinguished in the homozygote OO, the heterozygotes AO and BO are indistinguishable from the homozygotes AA and BB. In fact, therefore, the combinations produce only four phenotypes: A, B, AB and O. There are also two sub-groups of A known as A_1 and A_2, as well as other very rare sub-groups. The frequencies of the genotypes rather than of the phenotypes are used, giving the distribution of the genes A, B and O in populations; these frequencies are referred to as p, q and r.

Groups A and B tend to be concentrated in the middle of continental areas or in centres of dense population, while O is more marginal. In nearly every population, except for some tribes of American Indians, more than one blood group is present. Until very recently, there was no evidence that any one group was more advantageous than the others, but it has now been found that certain groups seem to offer protection against diseases. At first, only O and A seemed to show disease association, and these diseases were mostly psychosomatic (peptic ulcers, for instance) resulting, it is believed, from tension due mainly to overcrowding. In 1960, Pettenkofer & Bickerich discovered that there was an apparent association of smallpox vaccine with blood group A and of the agent causing plague with group H(O). They suggested that the relatively high incidence of group A in Western Europe and of group B in India might have been caused by selection due to plague and smallpox epidemics. It is, in fact, probable that the incidence of B in Asia may have increased in relatively recent times, but its frequency throughout the world is far lower than that of O or A.

The frequencies of the A, B and O genes throughout the world are estimated to be 21·5, 16·2, and 62·3 respectively. O has a high incidence in peripheral populations of north-western Europe, south-western Africa and parts of Australia and among isolated populations such as the Basques; in the New World, the Indians of Central and S. America and most of the tribes in N. America are almost entirely of group O.

The A group is high in Europe, especially in Scandinavia and the mountain systems of the Pyrenees, Alps and Carpathians (Fig. 4); in western Asia; and among the Murrayan aborigines of Australia. It reaches its maximum frequency among the Blackfeet Indians of Alberta. The distribution of the rare A_2 gene is particularly significant. In Europe it occurs in less than 10% of the population, except among the Lapps, where it attains its maximum frequency of up to 35%. Negroes show the same frequency of A_2 as the majority of Europeans. A_2 appears to be entirely absent from the indigenous populations of eastern Asia, Oceania and America.

The B group reaches its maximum in central Asia and northern India and is also high in Egypt and central Africa. In Europe, its frequency diminishes pro-

gressively from the borders of Asia westwards. It is believed that the B gene may
have been introduced to Europe by successive waves of Asiatic invaders between
the 5th and 15th centuries A.D. It is significant that the incidence of B is less than
3% among the Basques, who are survivors of the original pre-Indo-European

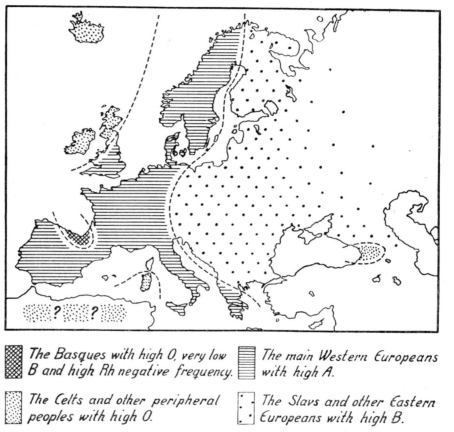

The Basques with high O, very low   The main Western Europeans
B and high Rh negative frequency.   with high A.

The Celts and other peripheral   The Slavs and other Eastern
peoples with high O.   Europeans with high B.

Fig. 4. Simplified distribution map of A B O blood-group frequencies in Europe.

After Darlington

population of Europe. Group B is almost entirely absent among the native populations of Australia and America. In view of the presumed Asiatic origin of the
American Indians, the almost complete absence of B in indigenous peoples other
than the Eskimos is rather surprising. It is possible that B may have been eliminated through genetic drift during the last 10,000 years or so in which the Ameri-

can Indians have been isolated. Alternatively, and more probably, the incidence of B may have been much lower at the time when their ancestors migrated across the Bering Straits.

In attempting to account for the present distribution, it seems most reasonable to assume that O and A were common in early man and that B was rare. The Mongoloids were almost certainly one of the last major stocks to become differentiated and it is among them that the incidence of B is highest.

The ABO frequencies can be nearly the same in unrelated populations in different parts of the world. By themselves, the A B O groups are insufficient to distinguish between races, but their distribution can be of great significance when considered in conjunction with that of the other blood groups, particularly the rhesus system and the M N Ss groups. For example, the Greenland Eskimos agree closely with Australian aborigines in the distribution of the A B O groups, yet they differ profoundly in M and N frequencies.

The Rhesus Series

In 1940, Landsteiner and Wiener discovered that rabbit serum injected with blood of the rhesus monkey would agglutinate certain human bloods. This discovery had important results in conquering haemolytic disease of the new-born which occurs occasionally where a rhesus positive child is born to a rhesus negative mother, the father having been rhesus positive. In such cases, the red cells in the child are destroyed by antibodies set up in the mother's system, while the mother too may be adversely affected by the blood group of the foetus.

The rhesus series depends on three adjacent loci on each of a pair of chromosomes; either of two alternative genes can occur at each locus. These alleles are expressed in several ways, but perhaps the simplest to follow is the system in which they are known as Cc, Dd and Ee. This results in the following possible gene combinations: CDe, cDE, cDe, Cde, cdE, CdE, CDE and the rhesus negative cde. Certain other very rare genes also occur.

The rhesus negative genotype, which is recessive, is distributed in northwestern Europe with an incidence of about 40% and is present among some Negroids, but is very rare or almost non-existent in the rest of the world. This genotype, so characteristic of Caucasoids, seems to have been derived from a pre-Indo-European stock, of which the Basques are the only known surviving example. Its frequency is higher among the Basques than any other people, reaching more than 50%. It is also high among Berbers of the Great Atlas, who on linguistic grounds are believed to be related to the Basques.

The groups with the highest frequency in northern and central Europe are cde and CDe; in the Mediterranean region, the incidence of the rhesus negative decreases considerably, while CDe increases. In Africa south of the Sahara, cde has a frequency of about 20%; but the Negroids are characterized by a unique preponderance of cDe, which reaches 60% or more in some tribes.

The rare gene D^u in the combination of cD^ue is also highly characteristic of Africa, where it has an average frequency of 6% in every population tested for it. Apart from among a few peoples in the eastern Mediterranean area, D^u is almost unknown outside Africa (Mourant, 1954). A gene known as V, which also forms part of the rhesus system, has a frequency of 20% in several African populations and less than 1% in all others studied so far (Mourant, 1959).

Distributions in south-western Asia and most of India are similar to those of the Mediterranean. In eastern Asia and the Pacific islands, the gene d is absent or very rare; in these areas the highest frequencies are CDe and cDE, while cDe and CDE also occur. The latter rare group is particularly common among the Australian aborigines. It is interesting that the distribution of rhesus types in the Australians resembles both that of the Caucasoids and the Mongoloids; the Australoids are considered to be derived from an archaic White stock in Asia. The gene d is also rare or absent among American Indians and Eskimos; both these people have high and approximately equal frequencies of CDe and cDE. A high incidence of cDE is confined to these people and to the Polynesians, suggesting a common ancestry (or migrations between Polynesia and America).

The rhesus series promises to be most useful in the study of racial relationships when more information about the distribution of the rarer groups has been collected. The Henshaw and Hunter genes are closely linked with the rhesus system as is also the factor known as V; in the series so far studied both are almost, if not exclusively, confined to Africans (Mourant, 1959). It is probable that other rhesus genes remain to be discovered and very likely it will be found that this great polymorphism or variability has some adaptive value in combating disease.

The M, N, Ss Groups

The frequencies of M and N vary less than those of the A B O groups and the rhesus series; their distribution throughout the world is about 55% M and 45% N.

The main exceptions are the Pacific islanders, Australians and Ainu with a considerably higher incidence of N, and the American Indians and Eskimos with a higher incidence of M. In Europe, an area of rather higher M frequencies extends from the East Baltic countries through European Russia to south-eastern Asia. The highest incidence of N in Europe is found among the Lapps and N is also fairly high among the North African Berbers.

Closely linked to the locus occupied on the chromosomes by M or N is another locus carrying S or s. The Ss group has been of most value anthropologically in distinguishing between the high N people of the Far East. S is almost completely absent among the Australian aborigines, but in New Guinea—where the incidence of N is highest—S is present in 23% of the population. Its incidence is also relatively high among the Ainu and the inhabitants of the Marshall Islands in Micronesia. In Europe, half the M genes carry S and half carry s; but of the N genes, only one-sixth carry S. In Africa, S is rarer still; but a gene known as S^u has been found only in Africans.

Other Blood-Group Studies

Of the other blood-group systems, several may prove extremely useful in anthropology when more data are available. The Diego factor, for instance, occurs only in certain groups of Mongoloids and people of Asiatic descent such as the American Indians. In the Duffy system there are two alleles, Fy^a and Fy^t; the gene Fy^a is found in 40% of Europeans, though among the Lapps the frequency is higher, as it is also among some Asiatics, rising to 90% in the Chinese, whereas it is very low among Africans. The Henshaw and Hunter antigens are commonest in Africa. An antigen known as Js, which has been discovered recently and which appears to be independent of the other systems, has proved to be peculiar to Africans (Mourant, 1959).

Using modern techniques, blood grouping has also been attempted on soft tissues of mummies and on ancient bones, since any remaining antigenic substances can be expected even in bone tissue. Obviously, bones which are mineralized can not be expected to contain such substances, as usually no organic matter then remains. So far, results have only been obtained for the ABO system, and even in this case there is still much debate as to the reliability of some of the determinations since contaminating agents may seriously affect the results

(Glemser, 1963). An example of the kind of information which can be obtained from prehistoric skeletons is given by Kennedy (1964) on Mesolithic and Neolithic burials from Gua Cha, Malaya; the A antigen had the highest frequency in both series (though this is not a characteristic feature of the modern serological map of south-east Asia) and B was also well represented, as it is today.

More Biochemical Characters

Apart from the blood groups, a number of other genetical characters have also been used in distinguishing between races. They include abnormal haemoglobins, haptoglobins and enzyme deficiencies. Such individualities in human biochemistry and their frequency distributions will certainly be studied far more intensively in the future.

Abnormal Haemoglobins

The incidence of abnormal haemoglobins, which attains high frequencies in certain populations, seems to be the result of selection due to environmental factors, particularly malaria. The genes responsible for four such abnormalities are: thalassaemia; sickle-cell; haemoglobin C (which is almost entirely restricted to West Africa); and haemoglobin E (which has a wide distribution in south-east Asia). The homozygotes of haemoglobins C and E are mildly anaemic; but individuals carrying both C and the sickle-cell gene, and those with both E and thalassaemia, are more severely affected.

The form of anaemia known as thalassaemia is fairly common in certain populations. This disease is almost confined to people of Mediterranean origin. In Italy marked regional differences in distribution have been observed. It occurs in two forms, mild and severe, both of which may be present in the same family. In the homozygous condition, the allele gives rise to severe and usually fatal anaemia. The heterozygote may or may not have symptoms, but the condition is readily recognizable in blood examinations. Most homozygotes die in childhood and few leave offspring. But there is probably some advantage of the heterozygote over the normal person, otherwise the trait would die out through natural selection. Probably the heterozygotes are more resistant to malaria, as is the case with heterozygous carriers of the sickle-cell trait.

The sickle-cell trait is caused by an abnormal haemoglobin resulting in distortion of the red blood cells into sickle-shaped forms when placed in a medium deficient of oxygen. The trait, which depends on a single gene, is almost entirely confined to Negroids, though it occurs also in the Veddoids of India and Ceylon and has occasionally been found in Persia, Arabia and Greece.

The sickle-cell trait is a good example of balanced polymorphism. Polymorphic genes are those which may occur on the same site on a chromosome but vary in their nature in different individuals. Polymorphism maintained by natural selection is called balanced polymorphism. Through this process, any gene which produces superior fitness in the heterozygote is maintained, even if it should be lethal in the homozygous form. In the homozygous state, the sickle-cell allele usually causes severe anaemia, the individual possessing about 90% abnormal haemoglobin. The heterozygous individual has about 50% abnormal haemoglobin but does not suffer any physical disability and in fact this state seems to provide resistance to malaria. In areas of malarial intensity, the proportion of sicklers reaches and maintains an equilibrium when the death rate from anaemia exactly counterbalances the death rate from malaria. It has been estimated that in these areas the heterozygous sickler has 16% greater chance of survival than the 'normal' person.

Some African populations contain up to 40% sicklers. The distribution, however, is rather patchy and tribes with very high and very low frequencies of the sickle-cell trait sometimes live in the same area (in some cases the tribes with a low incidence of sickling may be relatively recent immigrants). The incidence is highest among the Bantu of East Africa and becomes progressively lower towards the west and south; it is absent in the Bushmen.

The sickle-cell trait is no longer regarded as particularly useful in solving problems of African origins and affinities; the distribution of the cDe rhesus combination is now considered more significant in this respect.

Haptoglobins and Enzyme Deficiencies

The haptoglobins, a group of proteins in the plasma or serum, occur as three types known as 1–1, 2–1 and 2–2. These types are determined by a pair of allelic genes Hp^1 and Hp^2 (the genotype of 1–1 is $Hp^1 Hp^1$; of 2–1 it is $H^2 Hp^1$; and of 2–2 it is $Hp^2 Hp^2$). The Hp^1 frequency in western Europe ranges around 40%, but drops to only 28% in some Lapps. In most Asiatic populations the frequencies are even lower, ranging from about 10% to 25%. In central Africa, on the other hand, Hp^1 frequencies are very high, often around 50%, but they fall significantly among the Bushmen. Very broad racial distribution patterns can thus be distinguished.

Enzyme deficiencies resulting in abnormalities of the red blood cells show considerable variations, but are not particularly useful as racial indicators. One such deficiency is due to the low activity of the enzyme G6PDD (glucose-6-phosphate dehydrogenase); it has a wide distribution in tropical countries where malignant tertian malaria is present, as in the case of the abnormal haemoglobins.

Secretors and Non-secretors

Most individuals of blood groups A, B and AB have the corresponding antigens present in their saliva, while most individuals of group O—as well as many people of other groups—secrete an antigen known as H. The power to secrete any of the antigens A, B or H is due to the presence of a gene denoted S; this is dominant, as regards secretion, to its alleles (these are in no way connected with the alleles Ss of the MNS blood groups system). There appear to be certain racial differences in the frequencies of secretors and non-secretors; throughout Europe generally, the frequency of the S gene is about 50%, but reaches 63% among the Finns; among American Negroes it is 38% and nearly 100% in North American Indians (Mourant, 1954).

Another quite different substance secreted by the body also shows racial variations in frequency. Known as BAIB (B-amino-isobutyric acid), it is present in the urine in varying amounts. Frequencies range from 10% in U.S.A. Whites to 80% in inhabitants of the Marshall Islands. The reasons for this variability are unknown.

Tasting of P T C

The ability to taste phenylthiourea or phenylthiocarbamide (PTC) is probably due to the action of a single gene T which is dominant to a non-tasting gene t. To tasters, PTC is intensely bitter. There is a higher frequency of tasters among women than men; and chimpanzees have been found to include similar proportions of tasters and non-tasters as human beings. Nearly all American Indians have proved to be tasters. Among European populations, the incidence of tasters is highest among the Lapps. There are more tasters among the Egyptians and south-western Asiatics than among most Europeans other than the Lapps.

V

Racial Origins

The appearance and way of life of early man may be reconstructed both by the study of his bones and artifacts and by observations on the features and cultures of living primitive peoples. This chapter is concerned mainly with the origin of races in so far as they may be traced from fossil skeletal remains, from the beginning of the Palaeolithic or Old Stone Age over a million years ago to the end of the Ice Age 10,000 years ago.

One of the basic principles of evolution is that all features do not evolve at the same rate. Man's pelvis and limb bones became adapted for walking erect long before his brain grew relatively larger than that of the apes. The increased size of the brain-case and height of the vault of the skull, with its consequences on the whole shape of the head and face, is the most striking feature of the early stages of man's evolution. Since the end of Pleistocene times, however, the size of the brain has certainly not increased and in fact may have decreased; many of the Upper Palaeolithic people had larger brains than their descendants. Other important modifications have been a decreased thickness in the walls of the skull; the growth of a projecting chin; the reduction in size of the jaws; and the reduction of ridges of bone which had served to reinforce the attachment of powerful jaw- and neck-muscles.

The bony brow-ridges or supra-orbital torus for the attachment of muscles used in chewing were characteristic of early man and survived into Upper Pleistocene times. Extinct races such as Neanderthal Man had many such specialized features, whereas modern man, like his early ape ancestors, is essentially unspecialized. The Australian aborigines are nearest to the specialized Upper Pleistocene races (Fig. 5). Australoids, and to a lesser degree Caucasoids, have 'mature' (gerontomorphic) or rugged faces, whereas Negroids and particularly Mongoloids have 'infantile' (pedomorphic) faces which are more advanced in the evolutionary sense.

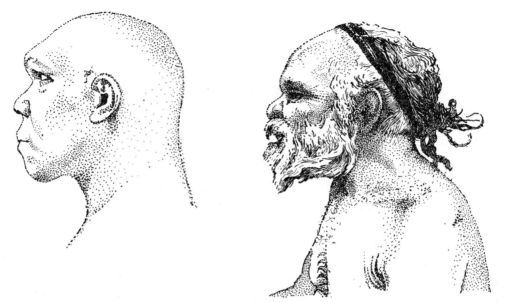

Fig. 5. Reconstruction of Rhodesian Man, with prominent brow-ridges and other specialized features characteristic of extinct types of early man. The Australian aborigines of today exhibit some of these features.

Rhodesian Man based on a reconstruction by Maurice Wilson; Australian aborigine based on a photograph

The Earliest Hominids

During the later part of the Lower Pleistocene and the early Middle Pleistocene, about a million years ago, several distinct races of hominids can already be distinguished. This is the earliest known stage in the evolution of the hominids, the family to which Man belongs. The brain of the creatures known as the Australopithecines was not appreciably larger than that of a modern ape, though in comparison with their total size it was relatively larger. These Australopithecines stood fully erect, leaving the hands free to handle tools. They are known to have lived in S. and E. Africa, in Java and in Palestine. Some were unspecialized (*Australopithecus africanus*) and lightly built; others (*A. robustus*) were heavier, with large grinding teeth suited to a diet which required much chewing.

There has been a tendency to 'split' early man into too many genera and species largely owing to the fact that, as the material is so scanty, enough allowance has not been made for individual and geographic variations. Some authorities, particularly in America, have now gone to the other extreme by maintaining that there never has been more than one genus of man. The majority of anthropologists and human palaeontologists now divide man into two genera: *Australopithecus* and *Homo*. Opinions are still widely divided as to how many species should be distinguished within these genera.

The *Homo erectus* (formerly known as *Pithecanthropus*) or second stage of man's evolution, during the Middle Pleistocene, is represented by several distinct races in widely separated parts of the world, *Homo erectus erectus* and *H. erectus modjokortensis* (or *robustus*) in Java, *H. erectus pekinensis* in China and *H. erectus mauritanicus* in North Africa. A similar skull was found recently at Olduvai Gorge, Tanganyika. By this time, the brain had evolved considerably from the Australopithecine level; but the vault of the cranium was still low, the brow-ridges very strongly developed, and the chin receding.

Only one human fossil of comparable age is known from Europe; it consists of a massive jaw from Mauer near Heidelberg and dates from an interstadial of the second glacial period, about 400,000 years ago. A fragmentary skull from Swanscombe in Kent dates from the succeeding interglacial, about 250,000 years ago. It is similar to a more complete and roughly contemporary skull from Steinheim in Germany, which is the first recognizable ancestor of *Homo sapiens*. Both the Steinheim and the Swanscombe skulls have a number of features more like modern man than the 'classic' Neanderthalers.

Specialized Races of the Upper Pleistocene

During the early part of the Würm glaciation, which began about 70,000 years ago, the Neanderthal race occupied parts of Europe, western and central Asia, and North Africa. Probably somewhat later, Rhodesian Man lived in Africa south of the Sahara, while Solo Man is known from Java. These three forms are rather similar, though Rhodesian and Solo Man are closer to *Homo erectus* and Neanderthal Man is more progressive as far as brain size is concerned.

Rhodesian Man is remarkable for the enormous development of the brow-ridges, which form a continuous bar or torus below the low, receding forehead. The face is long and prognathous and the palate very deep. African equivalents of the Neanderthal race are sometimes referred to as proto-Australoids, which does not imply that they are near relations of the Australian aborigines but does mean they share some rather similar features.

There seems little doubt that in Java there is a direct line of descent from

Homo erectus to Solo Man, who had a strongly developed supra-orbital torus like his contemporary in Africa. A fragmentary skull-cap with heavy brow-ridges found at Mapa, in Kwantung province, southern China, in 1958 is probably a similar form and is an intermediate link in the chain from *H. erectus pekinensis* to the skulls from the Upper Cave at Choukoutien (p. 47).

The 'classic' Neanderthalers are also remarkable for their heavy brow-ridges, low sloping foreheads and heavy jaws with receding chins. Their brain size averaged 1,450 c.c., which is 50 c.c. more than that of the average modern European. At Mount Carmel in Palestine there were two distinct groups: one, from Tabun, consists of typical 'classic' Neanderthalers; another, from Skhūl nearby, includes individuals showing a blend of features, part Neanderthal and part modern man. One explanation is that these were hybrids but it now seems that Tabun may have been earlier than Skhūl. Neanderthal Man, together with his cousins in Rhodesia and Java, became extinct about 40,000 years ago. Presumably his distinctive genes were gradually eliminated by natural selection and it seems that men of modern appearance occupied most parts of the Old World at about the same time.

Early Representatives of Modern Man
Europe

The earliest skull of completely modern type comes from Combe Capelle in south central France and was associated with the first stage of the Upper Palaeolithic of western Europe. A skull of approximately the same age from Chatelperron has extremely thick walls and is remarkable in being brachycephalic; nearly all other early Upper Palaeolithic skulls are long and narrow.

The well-known Cro-Magnon people, associated with the Aurignacian culture, were responsible for the earliest and some of the finest cave paintings in France. They were mostly tall, with long, narrow skulls and very large brain-cases allied to short, broad faces. The skull of the 'Old Man of Cro-Magnon' is particularly massive with a brain volume above the average of the modern European.

The Grimaldi burials from the Italian Riviera, also associated with an Aurignacian industry, are rather different from other Cro-Magnons. They consist of a woman and a boy aged about 15 with large teeth, very marked prognathism, and a broad nose. The forearms and shins are extremely long. The proportions of the limb bones, as well as the prognathism of the face, the bulging forehead and poorly developed brow-ridges, are typically Negroid characters.

Africa

The Cro-Magnons are very similar to the Upper Palaeolithic people of North Africa, known particularly from skeletons from Afalou bou Rummel and Mechta el Arbi in Algeria. The brow-ridges are strongly developed and the nose broader than in the European Cro-Magnons. The Berbers of North Africa are close to this type.

Skulls associated with late Upper Palaeolithic or Mesolithic industries in the Kenya rift valley are typically Caucasoid and show no trace of Negroid traits, which do not appear until much later. The earliest recognizable Negroid skeleton comes from Asselar near Timbuktu and probably dates from early in post-Pleistocene times. This individual was tall and slender, with particularly long shins and fore-arms. The skull is markedly dolichocephalic, the brow-ridges are poorly developed and the face broad. The nasal index is platyrrhine and the nasal bones are fused throughout their length, a rare feature observed most often among Negroes. Asselar man is not very like the modern West African Negro, however, and the fully differentiated Negro may have arisen more recently.

In South Africa, a line of descent can be traced from Rhodesian Man to a skull from Florisbad in South Africa with strongly marked brow-ridges. This type seems to be transitional between Rhodesian Man and the 'Boskop type'. First described from Boskop in the Transvaal, this type has since been distinguished at a number of sites in South Africa accompanied by Middle Stone Age industries—con-temporary with the late Upper Palaeolithic of Europe. The Boskop skull is dolichocephalic, pentagonal in shape when viewed from above, with a very large brain-case and small face. The Bushmen are sometimes regarded as diminutive descendants of the Boskopoids.

Asia, Oceania and Australia

Turning now to eastern Asia, in the Upper Cave of Choukoutien (which yielded the remains of Pekin Man) was found a remarkable family of Upper Pleistocene age. The old man of Choukoutien is in some ways astonishingly like the old man of Cro-Magnon, though the forehead and vault are lower. He is regarded as a member of the archaic White stock, of which the Ainu are modern representatives.

He was accompanied by two females: one of them shows typically Mongoloid features and her skull has even been compared with that of an Eskimo. The other woman was said to resemble the Melanesians. This is a good example of the pitfalls awaiting those who try to make rigid classifications. Types generally regarded as racially distinct clearly existed together within small groups in the past. Diversity seems to have been of very ancient origin and from such variable material the present populations became differentiated and diverged. Such early diversity is also illustrated by a skull from Niah Cave, Sarawak, dated by radio-carbon to about 40,000 years ago. This youth was rather lightly built and contrasts strongly with the rugged type represented by Solo Man, for instance.

Solo Man from the Upper Pleistocene of Java is probably ancestral to the Wadjak people of the same island, believed to be early post-Pleistocene in age. They were long-headed, with a huge palate and weak chin; they bear a striking resemblance to the Australian aborigines, though with a larger brain-case. A skull from Keilor near Melbourne is rather similar to, and roughly contemporary with, the Wadjak skeletons. It is important in showing that immigrants of the archaic White stock must have arrived in Australia at least by about 8,000 years ago.

In Malaya, associated with the Mesolithic Hoabinhian culture were burials of pygmy people with slender limbs, long heads, high-vaulted cranium and forehead, massive jaws and large teeth. They are not considered to be Negritos because the latter are essentially round-headed. They are rather similar to the Wadjak people and to the Veddoids of Southern India and Ceylon, but are said to resemble the Melanesians of New Caledonia most closely. The Melanesians must have migrated from Asia via the Malay Peninsula and there is little doubt that the Hoabinhians were their ancestors.

America

In America, human remains associated with Stone Age cultures and extinct fossil animals have been reported from various parts of the continent, but in most cases the geological evidence for dating has been questioned. One difficulty is that it is not yet clear at what date some of the extinct mammals died out. A human skeleton from Tepexpan in Mexico has been dated to about 10,000 years B.C. and is one of the oldest certainly dated human remains from the New World.

Tepexpan Man has been compared with the woman's skull from the Upper Cave at Choukoutien; both have the flat Mongoloid face, whereas many American Indians have typically prominent cheek-bones which probably reflect the archaic

White element in their ancestry. A skull from Midland, Texas, has also been dated to between 10,000 and 20,000 years old on the grounds of cultural and faunal associations and its antiquity has been supported by radio-carbon and uranium dating techniques.

An ancient skull from Punin in Ecuador appears to be rather different from the modern American Indians and is said to resemble the Australian aborigine. Other skeletons from Lagoa Santa, eastern Brazil, though dominantly of American Indian type, also have certain features reminiscent of the Australoids.

In general, the earliest skulls of the New World are relatively long-headed, the later ones are round-headed. The American Indians are believed to be the result of a mixture between archaic White and later Mongoloid immigrants from Asia; the first of these immigrants must have crossed the Bering Straits before the end of the Ice Age, probably by a land bridge which existed when the sea-level was lower.

The Food-gathering Stage

During most of the Stone Age, for about a million years or so, people must have lived in small, isolated groups. There were distinct tool-making techniques in different geographical areas, which suggest that the gene flow between these groups was rather limited. Among the Australian aborigines, it was rare to find tribes of more than 500 persons and Bushmen groups consist of 50–100 persons; probably this figure was about the upper limit of groups of prehistoric hunters. Since men at the hunting and food-gathering stage make extensive use of natural resources, it would have been impossible for more than one population to exist in the same territory. These small, isolated groups provided the ideal conditions for promoting rapid evolutionary changes.

Within such groups, mutations must have arisen which, even though they may have had no immediate adaptive advantages, would have increased in frequency by statistical accident. Some of these traits may have been encouraged through what Darwin called sexual selection, that is the selection of certain preferred characters in the choice of a mate. Size and strength and 'mature' characters may have been admired in men (and the strong would have obtained more wives than the weak), while women who remained small and 'unspecialized' were probably favoured. Sexual differences (dimorphism) are very marked in early hominids and also in the Upper Palaeolithic populations of Europe. Among

D

modern races, sexual dimorphism is most pronounced in the Australoids and Caucasoids and is least marked in the more recently differentiated Mongoloids.

Food-gathering peoples are still found in the extreme northern and southern fringes both of the New and the Old World. They include the Eskimos and the Fuegians; the Australian aborigines; the Veddoids of southern India and Ceylon; and the Negrito pygmies in the interior of the islands of Oceania, the Andaman Islands and parts of the mainland of southern Asia. The Bushmen of South Africa and the pygmies of the Congo forests may be remnants of an ancient population of Africa, perhaps reduced in size through harsh conditions and inadequate food. It is an interesting and unexplained fact that the Australian aborigines and the Bushmen, both of whom are hunters now living in deserts, are completely different in physical type; the first is 'gerontomorphic' or mature, the latter is 'pedomorphic' or infantile. In this case natural selection has favoured two opposite types in similar environments.

Probably all the major races we know today had differentiated before the end of Pleistocene times. With the ending of the Ice Age, evolution must have proceeded at an accelerated pace in the northern parts of the Old World as a result of drastic changes in vegetation and fauna, which put a premium on adaptability. Such ecological changes must have speeded up the formation of sub-races and most of the present sub-races certainly existed before the end of the food-gathering stage. The Mediterranean Proper sub-race, for instance, can be traced back to the Mesolithic Natufians of Palestine. So-called 'Upper Palaeolithic' types among the populations of Europe today are very unlikely to be pure descendants of the Cro-Magnons or other Upper Palaeolithic people, but are more likely to be the result of genetic recombinations or the re-emergence of old strains.

The Food-producing Stage

The process of change from a food-gathering to a food-producing way of life was a gradual one and must have begun in an experimental way in Mesolithic fishing communities, for fishermen are usually more settled than hunters. The earliest known Neolithic has been dated at Jericho to about 7000 B.C.—only some 500 generations ago. From the Middle East, the first agriculturalists and herdsmen spread out into Europe, North Africa, India and China. They reached all these areas at least by 3000 B.C. (much earlier in parts of Europe and in Egypt).

These farmers mixed with the indigenous people they found, people who had reached a state of biological equilibrium with their environment as a result of thousands of years of natural selection. From them, the invaders acquired genes well adapted to local conditions.

With the food supply becoming ever more assured, the population increased rapidly. As a result of extensive mixing of populations and tremendous numerical increase, many more sub-races were formed during the Neolithic stage, which of course began at different times in various parts of the world.

For the most part, the early farmers mixed with indigenous people who were also of the Caucasoid stock. But in China, where the local population was Mongoloid, this physical type prevailed and the immigrant Caucasoids were absorbed. The new farmers cultivated plants unknown in the west and better suited to a climate with summer rains; these plants were carried to Indochina, Siam, Burma and Indonesia. The food-gatherers of south-eastern Asia gave the invaders from the north a genetic structure able to withstand the hot, damp climate of the new environment (Coon, 1959).

The aborigines of India were probably of an archaic White stock. They imparted to the Dravidian-speaking and Aryan-speaking invaders a genetic constitution well suited to local conditions. The Mongoloids of Tibet, however, never spread south of the Himalayas since they were adapted to the cold of high altitudes and were unable to withstand the heat and damp of the plains.

The migrations of the Mediterranean race into Europe and its subsequent differentiation are discussed later (p. 59). Neolithic farmers spread along both northern and southern shores of the Mediterranean, as well as inland over the fertile soil of the Danube valley. In the extreme north of Europe and Asia, where agriculture was impossible, the people continued to depend on fishing and reindeer-herding for a livelihood. This basic culture is continuous from the Baltic to the Pacific.

In Africa south of the Sahara there are few recognizable signs of food production or domestication of animals before the spread of the knowledge of iron-working, which was diffused by Negroids some time after the first century A.D. In later times, the migrations of Hamitic-speaking pastoralists caused much racial admixture.

Food-producing in America is believed to have begun as early as 5000 B.C. in the South-West and Mexico, where squash, gourds and beans were cultivated; maize was first grown about 3000 B.C. On the Peruvian coast, there are signs of cultivation by 3000 B.C. and maize was grown by 700 B.C. It is thought that manioc, yams and other root crops were cultivated in the Amazon forests by this time if not earlier. In the Mississippi valley, pumpkins and sunflowers were grown for food by about 1000 B.C. (Willey, 1960). The agricultural American Indians have many more typically Mongoloid characters than the more rugged Marginal Indians who depended on hunting and fishing.

The Bronze and Iron Ages

The Bronze Age civilizations of the Middle East flourished from about 4000 to 2500 B.C. and only declined with the advent of iron-working. From its origins in Sumeria, the Early Bronze Age culture diffused to Egypt and to India. In most of Europe, the Bronze Age culture lasted only for about 600 years. During this time, trade of bronze objects for amber and other local commodities meant much travel by merchants and mixture with the people they came across. At this time, too, the climate was becoming drier and forests gave way to open country, allowing people to spread into new areas and encouraging pastoral nomadism. Nomadic horsemen from western Asia invaded Mesopotamia and Egypt, where the whole kingdom was conquered by the Hyksos. At the same time, seafarers from the eastern Mediterranean followed the route of the Neolithic megalith builders to Spain, France, Britain and Scandinavia.

Unfortunately for anthropologists, cremation was practised increasingly during the Bronze Age, and almost exclusively towards the end of this period. Racial knowledge of this important period of expansion is therefore rather meagre. It is certain, however, that the spread of the early metal cultures had profound effects on the physical type of the people who were conquered by these invaders with superior weapons.

During the early Iron Age, there was even more mixture of the Caucasoid peoples as a result of invasions and warfare. The decay and overthrow of the Classical Mediterranean civilizations by hordes of vigorous barbarians was completed by about 500 A.D., and during this time interbreeding between populations hitherto far apart was widespread. This period of invasions by Celts and others was followed during the next thousand years by successive waves of Mongoloid intrusions into Europe, which had a profound effect on the population of the eastern and central parts of the continent.

The urban way of life, during the Bronze Age and more particularly during the Iron Age, resulted in a tremendous increase in infectious and contagious diseases and perhaps also in nutritional deficiencies due to an unbalanced diet. Natural selection would have operated strongly in such close-knit communities, eliminating the unfit. The division of labour or 'occupational selection' also began to bring about the differentiation of physical types into classes and castes. No longer was there such a premium on strength and endurance; now almost for the first time in the long history of man useful sedentary occupations could be found for intellectuals and those of less robust physique.

Recent Colonizations

To complete this very brief survey of racial origins, mention must be made of the colonists of the past five centuries who have had a profound effect on the indigenous inhabitants in many parts of the world. The great age of discovery and migration was, of course, the 16th century; from that time onwards, the first European settlers landed in America, South Africa, Australia and New Zealand. The Caucasoid colonizers were enterprising, fit people and probably on the whole genetically superior to the average stay-at-home. New environments—climates and foods—brought about considerable changes even in the first generation of descendants of these immigrants. About 20 generations separate the people of today from their pioneer forefathers and new types have become stabilized.

The effect of these colonizers on the aborigines of the countries they settled in was immense. The cultural gap between the two was so great that fusion between them was often impossible. The aboriginal populations were much reduced by warfare and the introduction of European diseases; either they retreated to deserts and other inhospitable areas or became extinct. The present trend, however, is for survivors to face absorption rather than extinction; this is happening, for instance, with the American Indians and the Australian aborigines. In South Africa, the absorption happened earlier; the mixture of Dutch with Hottentots, for instance, gave rise to the Cape Coloured population.

Among the 30 living races of the world distinguished by Coon *et al.* (1950) they list the 'North American Coloured', 'South African Coloured', 'Ladino' (a mixture of American Indian and Mediterranean) and 'Neo-Hawaiian', a blend in process of formation and stabilization in the Hawaiian islands consisting of

Mongoloid, Caucasoid and diffuse 'Negroid' (Melanesian) elements added to the Polynesian. To those who regret the fact that many distinctive races will soon cease to exist, it may be some comfort to know that the process of race-formation is still going on. It has always been a continuous process, but no doubt the time will come when the population of the world is so immense that no isolated groups can survive anywhere.

VI

Caucasoids

The name 'Caucasoid' was first used by Blumenbach in the late 18th century in his studies on peoples of the Caucasus region. This area, between the Black Sea and the Caspian, was probably the original homeland of many of the populations of Europe today and it is one of the most complex areas of the world from a racial point of view. Blumenbach's term has come to be applied to the stock which is sometimes referred to as White (though it includes many people of dark brown skin colour) or European (though it includes also people of Arabia, Iran and India as well as of North and East Africa).

Characteristics of the Caucasoids are as follows: skin colour ranging from white to dark brown; hair usually wavy, but ranges from straight to curly; facial and body hair generally rather abundant; all shapes of head occur; nose comparatively narrow and prominent; lips thin; face straight or orthognathous; forehead high; chin well developed.

Blood-group characters include the presence of the A_2 gene and relatively high frequencies of the rhesus negative gene cde and of the MS combination. In Europe, there is a systematic change in rhesus frequencies southwards towards the Mediterranean; going eastwards, there is a change in MN frequencies, with higher M east of the Baltic and in Russia. The incidence of B also increases eastwards, while O, which is most frequent in peripheral areas of the north-west, decreases eastwards.

The principal race of the Caucasoid stock is the Mediterranean; many other groups which have been classified in the past as separate races may be regarded as variants of the Mediterranean Race. This race stretches from the Atlantic to India, on both sides of the Mediterranean and down into the Horn of Africa. It merges into Mongoloids in the east, Negroids in Africa, and Veddoids in India.

Although the main language group of the Caucasoids is Indo-European, members of this stock speak also Ural-Altaic (Uralic includes Finnic, Ugrian and Samoyedic; Altaic includes Turkish); Euskarian (the language of the Basques);

55

Dravidian (in southern India); Hamitic and Semitic (in North and East Africa and Arabia).

Racial classification proved far more difficult in the case of the Caucasoids than of any of the other stocks. This is partly because we know more about them from archaeological material and historical records, with a resultant tending towards minor subdivision. But mainly it is because of the age-long wanderings of the energetic Mediterranean peoples, who mixed extensively with the indigenous inhabitants over a vast territory and thus brought into being a large number of distinctive populations.

Most approaches to a scheme of classification in Europe were founded on a few main differences in physical features, particularly pigment and head shape, related to distinct geographical zones. Thus three main horizontal belts were distinguished in Europe: the blond Nordics and East Baltics in the north, the first long-headed and the second round-headed; a zone of round-headed brunets—the Alpines, Dinarics and Armenoids—in the centre; in the south, long-headed brunets of the Mediterranean Proper sub-race, joining on to the Irano-Afghans in western Asia (Fig. 6).

Bearing in mind that no rigid boundaries can be drawn between 'types', which are constantly changing, it is convenient to outline in very broad terms some of the main characteristics of various populations. With the exception of the East Baltics and the Lapps, Caucasoids may be regarded as variants of the Mediterranean Race, in which the following 'types' may be distinguished:

Europe

(1) *Early Mediterranean*, now represented only by the Basques. Distinctive owing to their unique blood-group pattern and pre-Indo-European language.

(2) *Mediterranean Proper*, represented by such people as the Arabs and Spaniards. Light build, medium stature, rather long head, brunet complexion.

(3) *Irano-Afghan*, represented mainly in Iran, Afghanistan, Baluchistan and north-western India. Heavy build, large and long head, high-bridged and long nose, abundant beard and body hair. Apart from pigment, they are of the same physical type as Nordics.

    (a) *Atlanto-Mediterranean* type. Similar to Irano-Afghan in build, long head, rugged features. The type of the megalith builders. Now found

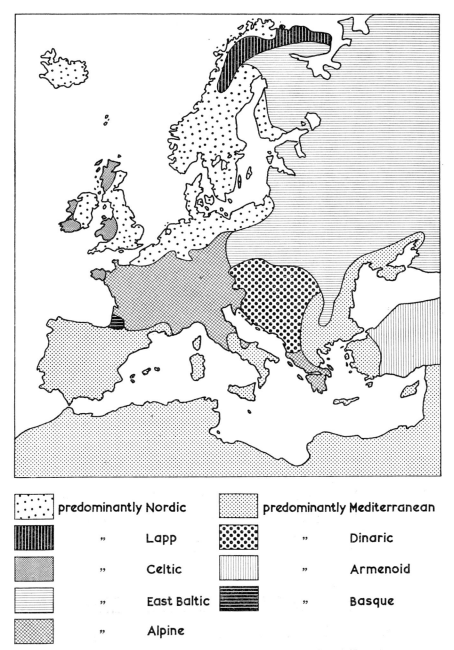

⠿	predominantly Nordic		⠿	predominantly Mediterranean
▓	„	Lapp	▓	„ Dinaric
▓	„	Celtic	▓	„ Armenoid
▓	„	East Baltic	▓	„ Basque
▓	„	Alpine		

Fig. 6. Simplified distribution map of the peoples of Europe.

typically among the Berbers of North Africa and in individuals from Greece to Spain and the British Isles. Often associated with blondism.

(b) *Dinaric* type. Large, round head, flattened at the back (often artificially); prominent hooked nose; long face; tall stature. Represented by various peoples east of the Adriatic.

(c) *Armenoid* type. Similar to Dinaric, but with more exaggerated features. Very prominent hooked nose with depressed tip; head flattened at the back (again, usually artificially); full lips; abundant beard and body hair. Found in Armenia and north-eastern Turkey.

(4) *Nordic*. Tall, blond, long head, long face, narrow nose, deep chin. Typically found in Sweden and East Norway.

   (a) The 'Celtic Iron Age' type with low forehead is a variant which survives mainly in Ireland and Scotland.

(5) *Alpine*. Round head, thick-set build, sallow complexion, broad nose with blobby tip. Represented by some of the French, Bavarians, Swiss and northern Italians.

(6) *East Baltics*. Round-headed, very blond people of countries east of the Baltic who originated in Asia and speak Finno-Ugrian languages. Include many of the Balts, Finns, Poles and Russians.

(7) *Lapps*. Short stature, very short legs, round head, broad face, small jaws and teeth, broad concave nose. Highly individual blood-group frequencies.

India

(8) *Southern group*. Dark-skinned populations of south-eastern India (excluding the Veddoids) and North Ceylon, speaking Dravidian languages.

(9) *'Mediterranean' Indians*. Lighter-skinned, lightly built, long-headed typically Mediterranean populations such as the Hindus, forming the largest group in India and speaking Indo-European languages. (The Irano-Afghan type is also represented in north-western India.)

North and North-eastern Africa

(10) *Northern group* includes the Hamitic-speaking Berbers, mostly of Atlanto-Mediterranean type.

(11) *Eastern group* includes the Egyptians and the Semitic- and Hamitic-speaking inhabitants of the Horn of Africa (Ethiopia and Somalia) who are mixed with Negroids in varying degrees.

The Mediterranean Race: Its Differentiation into Sub-races

From the beginning of Neolithic times the Mediterranean Race was by far the most important in the history of the western civilized world. The little Mediterranean people, whose ancestors were the Mesolithic Natufians of Palestine, spread out from their original home in the Middle East before 5000 B.C., transmitting their knowledge of farming and also their features over North Africa and Europe. One branch went along the north coast of the Mediterranean, another along the south coast; eventually they reached France, Switzerland and the British Isles, diffusing the culture known as Western Neolithic. Skeletally, these people are exemplified by the ancient Egyptians (and the modern Egyptians have altered hardly at all during the past 5,000 years).

Another branch migrated up the valley of the Danube, practising a shifting slash-and-burn cultivation and transmitting the culture known as Danubian. Both the Danubians and the Western Neolithic people were short, lightly built, long-headed and with relatively little sexual dimorphism. A similar physical type migrated eastwards to India and forms the basis of most of the present inhabitants of that country. The Arabs are the most typical examples of this sub-race, the *Mediterranean Proper*.

The taller, heavier-boned, long-headed *Atlanto-Mediterranean* type, showing marked sexual dimorphism, is near to the Upper Palaeolithic people of western Europe and North Africa. This was also the type of the megalith builders of late Neolithic times, who sailed from the Mediterranean up the Atlantic coasts of Spain and France to the British Isles and Scandinavia. This physical type is important today in North Africa and the British Isles.

The Basques, who are believed to be the only pure descendants of the early Neolithic population of Europe still surviving, may be considered to be members of an *Early Mediterranean* sub-race.

The *Irano-Afghan* sub-race and the very similar *Nordics* probably both arose somewhere near the Black Sea.

The Alpines. The people discussed so far all had long or medium-length heads. The round-headed *Alpines* are in other respects very similar to Mediterranean peoples. This round-headed element re-emerged not only in the Alpine region but also in the Caucasus, Anatolia, the Syrian highlands and the Armenian plateau. These areas were not important highways for movements of Mediterranean peoples, but refuge areas.

Dinarics and Armenoids. The well-known hooked nose, sloping forehead, eyebrows meeting in the middle, and heavy beard represented in Bronze Age sculptures and other forms of art of the Middle Eastern civilizations is a type which must have been ancestral to the present *Dinarics* and *Armenoids*. These people are characterized by round heads, artificially flattened in the occipital region as a result of 'cradling' of infants by strapping them to a cradle-board. The Dinaric type is believed to have originated in the Middle East around 2000 B.C., whence it spread to Spain and became associated with the Bell Beaker culture of Early Bronze Age times; this culture was later diffused to the Rhineland and central Europe. The Armenoids are closely related to the Irano-Afghans and both may possibly have acquired their round head from crossing with Alpines.

Caucasoids in Europe

(1) Early Mediterranean: the Basques

The Basques (Fig. 7) are unique in being apparently almost pure survivors of the prehistoric population of Europe. Descended from Neolithic pastoralists, they have remained isolated and, until recent times, inbred ever since. Their speech, Euskarian, is a non-Indo-European language and is linked with that of the Ligurians, the first historically recorded inhabitants of Switzerland. The former wide distribution of these people is indicated by place-names incorporating *asca* or *asco*, for instance, Gascony, the country of the Vasconi or Basques. The Ligurians were displaced by the Celts, the first carriers of Indo-European speech.

About three-quarters of a million Basques live in northern Spain and southwestern France (there are also a great many in South America). They are medium in stature, lightly built, with broad shoulders and narrow hips. The skull is mesocephalic with measurements very close to the Celtic Iron Age type (p. 68). Characteristic features include a prominent, thin nose; very narrow face; pointed, narrow chin (strikingly similar to that of the pre-pottery Neolithic inhabitants of Jericho); vertical or slightly bulging forehead; poorly developed brow-ridges.

Although most Basques are brunet, there are more blonds among them than among other Mediterraneans with the exception of some Berber groups.

The blood-group frequencies of the Basques show wide deviations from the

Fig. 7. A Basque, with typical narrow face and narrow, prominent nose.

Based on a photograph by Hammerton

normal European pattern and emphasize the fact of their long isolation. They have the lowest incidence of group B in Europe—less than 3%—and the highest rhesus negative (cde) frequency, which is up to 50% in some communities.

(2) Mediterranean Proper

The type known as Mediterranean Proper, or Basic Mediterranean, is seen typically in the Arabs (Fig. 8), as well as Portuguese, Spaniards and Italians. The build is light or gracile, the head long or more often medium, skin colour light brown or olive, stature medium averaging 165 cm. (5 ft. 6 in.), nose straight or slightly convex. Among the earliest recognizable representatives are the Mesolithic Natufians of Palestine.

The Arabs of Arabia are confined mostly to the peripheral areas, owing to the extreme aridity of most of the country. Throughout history, vast numbers of people dispersed from Arabia to other regions. The early wanderings of the Jews; the settlement of north-eastern Africa by colonists from the Hadhramaut; the

occupation of parts of Somalia and Ethiopia by Sabaeans from the Yemen, resulting in the establishment of the state of Axum; and the enormous expansions
of Arabs after the death of Mohammed, particularly to North Africa, all had considerable effects on the populations of countries outside the Arab homeland. The
purest nucleus of the Mediterranean Proper sub-race today is to be found in the
Yemen. The Yemenis of the fertile plateau are slender and relatively long-legged,

Fig. 8. Characteristic of the Mediterranean Race are the lightly built, brown-skinned Arabs.

Based on a Shell photograph

with fairly long head, very long upper face, high forehead, and extremely
narrow nose. The Jews may have been composed originally of a small Mediterranean type similar to the present Yemeni Arabs; a taller, hook-nosed Irano-
Afghan strain; and Atlanto-Mediterranean elements contributed by the Philis-
tines (Coon, 1939). The Gypsies are also Mediterranean people who originated in
northern India. Blood-group evidence supports this theory; frequencies of blood
group B among gypsies, for instance, are well above average European levels,
amounting to 25% among gypsies in Hungary.

(3) Irano-Afghan

This type is common in Iran, Afghanistan and Baluchistan; it is present also
in north-western India (see p. 74). The Irano-Afghans have the large, dolicho-

cephalic Atlanto-Mediterranean head form, but differ principally in the long, high-bridged nose. The head is high, the face long, stature tall.

The Persians and Afghans have facial dimensions similar to the Nordics, but the upper face is longer. The Kurdish nomads of Iraq, Iran and Turkey, who include a blond minority, may be a mixture of Irano-Afghan and ancestral Nordics from the area of Iran. The Turkomans form another variety, differing in the extremely high vault of the cranium. Coon (1939) considered them to be descended from the early Caucasoids who migrated northwards into Mongolia, taking with them Altaic speech, agriculture and, later, horse nomadism.

A strong Irano-Afghan element, mixed with Atlanto-Mediterranean, is present in the inhabitants of Iraq. The population is much the same as it was in Sumerian and Babylonian times; the post-Islamic acquisition of Arab blood seems to have made little difference. The Iraqis are taller than the Arabs, with larger face, longer and broader nose, heavier jaw. Beard and body hair are very heavy, a trait which is characteristic of the Irano-Afghans as a whole.

This is perhaps as good a place as any to discuss the various peoples of the Caucasus, among whom is represented the Iranian type. Bunak (1960) recognizes no less than 16 well-established physical types in this area, which he divides into four main 'races' (sub-races or variants according to the terminology used in this book). These he calls the Caucasian, Pontic, Pontic-Zabrossian and Caspian. The Caucasians of western Transcaucasia include the Georgians; typically they are moderately brachycephalic, of medium stature, dark, with rather narrow face, narrow and often hooked nose, and abundant body hair. The Pontic 'race' (a new term) of the northern Caucasus includes the Adighe and Daghestan peoples and a central Terek group; the Adighe are mesocephalic, the Daghestan peoples are hyperbrachycephalic, while the Terek group are similar to the Georgians. The Pontic-Zabrossian type of the central highlands is that usually known as Armenoid. The Caspians of the south-east, who include the Azerbaidzhanis, extend far beyond the Caucasus region and are of the type generally known as Iranian.

Atlanto-Mediterranean type

This tall, straight-nosed, strongly dolichocephalic type forms the main element in the population of North Africa; it is represented in Palestine, Iraq, parts of Arabia and the East Balkans and turns up sporadically in individuals as far north as the British Isles. It was the type of some of the Upper Palaeolithic people of western Europe and of the megalith builders (p. 59), whose imprint on the populations of

Crete and the Balearic islands is still visible today. It also forms an important element in the composition of the Greeks and the Bulgars.

Among people of this physical type there is a tendency towards the unusual combination of dark hair and light eyes, as seen in many Irish and Scots, as well as the Riffian Berbers.

Dinaric type

Dinarics (Fig. 9) share many common features with Armenoids, notably the high, peaked head with artificially flattened occiput, long face and prominent nose. Dinaric features are more refined and less exaggerated, however, and there is a greater range of pigmentation than among the Armenoids. The black hair and dark brown eyes of the Armenoids rarely occur in Dinarics. These people include

Fig. 9. Dinaric type: a Rumanian from the Carpathians.

Based on a photograph by Raine

the Bosnians, Montenegrins, northern Albanians, Serbs, Croats, Slovenes and Tyrolese. They may have some Alpine, and possibly also Nordic, admixture but the Irano-Afghan strain is the most important. The Slovenes live the furthest west of the Southern Slavs; they arrived in their present territory during the 7th century A.D. and absorbed remnants of the Celtic and Illyrian populations. The Croats

I. The tremendous variety of the peoples of the Soviet Union is shown in these two pictures. *Top*, peasants of Latvia; the girl is typical of the East Baltic type. *Below*, athletes from Kazakhstan, east of the Caspian; the man on the right is a good example of the Turkic type.

Society for Cultural Relations with the U.S.S.R.

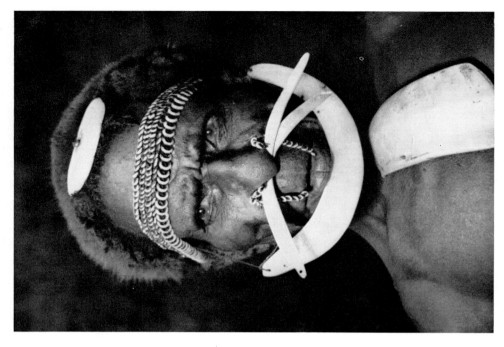

Camera Press

II. A Papuan bride and elder adorned with shell ornaments. In spite of their very dark skins, the Melanesians have a strong archaic White element in their make-up.

III. *Top*, a Maori student, member of the handsome Polynesian race. *Below*, Fijians from Lautoka with the frizzy hair typical of Melanesians.

IV. Tungus women of Evenk, classical Mongoloids with features adapted to extreme cold (*left*). An Eskimo of Canada (*right*); the Eskimos are closely related to the classical Mongoloids of Asia.

Left, *Society for Cultural Relations with the U.S.S.R.*   Right, *National Film Board of Canada*

V. A Tamil from southern India (*left*) and a Kayan warrior of Borneo (*right*) illustrate the contrast in the peoples of southern Asia.

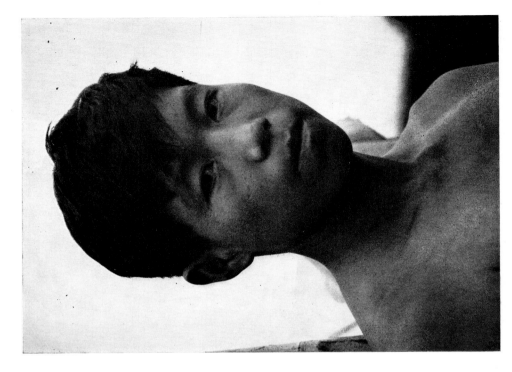

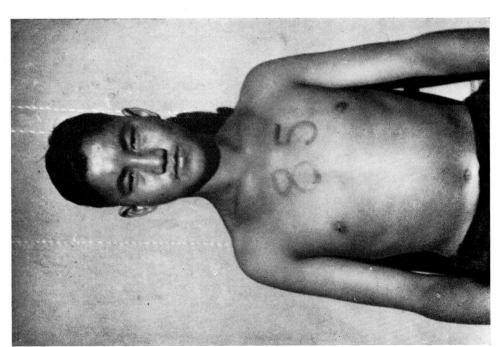

VI.   A Nepalese hillman (*left*) is surprisingly like a Jumbo boy from Ecuador (*right*).

Left, *Capt. P. A. Skoulding.*   Right, *Shell*

VII. Jivaro woman of Ecuador (*left*) and Maori fishwife (*right*). The resemblance between Polynesians and some American Indians is often marked; both show an admixture of archaic White and Mongoloid features.

Left, *Shell*.   Right, *New Zealand House*

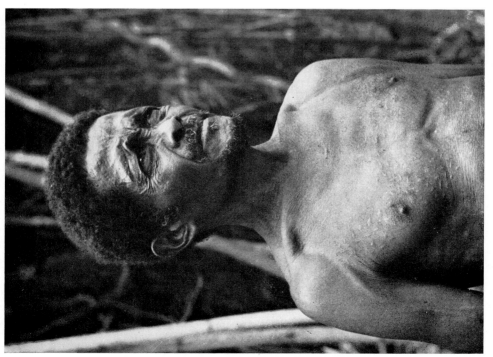

VIII. Aeta pygmy of Luzon, Philippines (*left*); Congo pygmy (*right*). A case of independent parallel evolution? Or a common aboriginal substratum in Africa, Asia and the Pacific?

IX. Bushman of the Kalahari. Note the peppercorn hair.

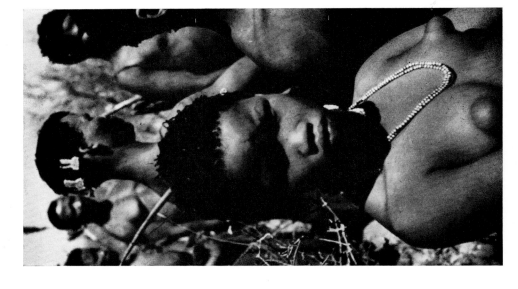

X. Bushwoman with very pronounced steatopygia (*left*); compare with woman of the Andaman Islands, Fig. 2. Bush girl from Ghanzi with protuberant areola, a characteristic of young Bushwomen (*right*).

Left, *Prof. R. A. Dart.*   Right, *Prof. P. V. Tobias*

XI. *Left*, A Hadendoa of Suakin, member of the Beja group of Eastern Hamites, who have 'fuzzy-wuzzy' hair like the Fijians (see Plate III). *Right*, A Samburu warrior of northern Kenya, closely related to the Masai; these people are known as Nilo-Hamites, implying a mixture of Nilotic Negro and 'Hamitic' blood.

Left, Shell.   Right, Mrs. Joy Adamson

XII. *Left*, a Mangbetu woman of the Congo with artificially deformed head. *Right*, Luba warrior, Congo; compare his features with those of the Papuan elder in Plate II (a case of parallel evolution?).

Left, *Shell*.　Right, *Planet News*

are intermediate between the Slovenes and the Serbs, who live mostly to the north and east of the main Alpine–Dinaric zone. The Bosnians and Montenegrins are exceptionally tall and heavy; the Montenegrins average 177 cm. in stature. The northern Albanians include the most extreme form of Dinaric.

Armenoid type

This composite type is very similar to the Irano-Afghan and to the Dinarics, but has a larger head, longer face, and broader nose. The head is very broad and pointed, the forehead slopes to an apex almost at the back of the vault, and the occiput drops away so steeply as to be almost vertical. This flattening of the back

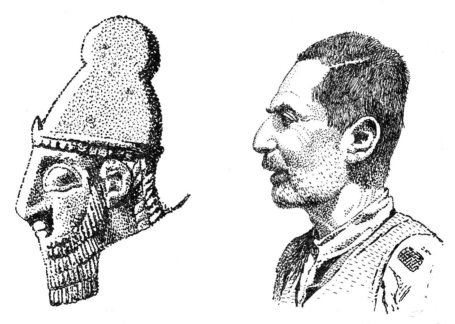

Fig. 10. The Armenoid type is characterized by a very prominent nose forming an almost continuous line with the forehead and by a flattened back to the head, often caused by artificial deformation in infancy. An ancient Hittite relief is compared with a Cretan peasant.

Based on photographs in Peake & Fleur

of the head is usually accounted for by 'cradling habits'—babies are swaddled and immobilized on their backs, resulting in artificial deformation of the skull. Other characteristics include the high-rooted hooked nose with depressed tip, full lips, abundant beard and body hair, and thick eyebrows usually meeting in the middle.

E

Body build is heavy, stature generally medium. Armenoids are found east and south-east of the Black Sea, in Armenia and north-eastern Turkey.

Sumerian, Babylonian, Assyrian and Hittite sculptures and other representations, from the 4th millennium B.C. onwards, clearly show the Armenoid forehead sloping in a continuous line with the beaky nose (Fig. 10). From its centre of development in Asia Minor, this physical type, which may have been ancestral to Irano-Afghans, Dinarics and Armenoids, spread southwards to Arabia and India. There is not much evidence of its extension into Europe in prehistoric and early historic times, though the Etruscans, who almost certainly originated in Asia Minor, may well have been of this type. They spoke a non-Indo-European language and settled in Italy during the 8th century B.C.

(4) Nordic

The differences between Nordics and Mediterraneans, and particularly Irano-Afghans, are mainly in size and pigmentation. Compared with the Mediterranean, the typical Nordic (Fig. 11) has a longer and narrower face, more prominent brow-ridges, a more sloping forehead, a longer, higher and narrower nose, and a more pronounced chin. The bones of a small Nordic are often indistinguishable from those of a large Mediterranean and so, as pigment cannot be determined from skeletons, it is difficult to estimate the date of the origin of the Nordics. They are considered to be the result of a mixture between Danubians of the Basic Mediterranean type and later invaders from the Caspian region (Coon, 1939). A minority of Nordics retain the brunet Mediterranean pigmentation: blondness presumably arose as the result of mutations and was preserved in northern areas where it had some selective advantage. Although blond hair and blue eyes are characteristic of younger Nordics, both hair and eyes tend to darken with age. It has been claimed that blondness is already to be seen in some Danish Bronze Age burials—preserved by the tannic acid in oak coffins—for instance the young woman from Egtved. It is possible, however, that the pigment may have faded.

Various Nordic sub-types have been distinguished; they include a tall, slender type, very long-headed, with light bones, sloping forehead, weak brow-ridges, long, narrow face, thin, high nose and deep jaws, which is found almost exclusively in Sweden and eastern Norway. The 'Anglo-Saxon' type of North Germany and England is heavier-boned and more rugged, with rounder head, less sloping forehead, coarser nose and more prominent cheek-bones.

From the Baltic area, the Nordic people expanded in successive waves, starting with the Teutons who pushed their way from Denmark to the Danube, Gaul and Italy. In this way Nordic blood was diffused throughout Europe during the first thousand years A.D. In Britain, successive invasions of Angles, Saxons, Jutes, Danes and Norsemen lasted from the 3rd to 9th centuries, after which the country was conquered by the Normans; by this time, the Normans themselves were predominantly of Nordic blood. Important invasions of Goths and Vandals occurred in Europe from the 3rd to the 5th centuries. Later the Vandals proceeded through

Fig. 11. A blond Nordic from Sweden.
Based on a photograph

France and Spain to Africa; the Bavarians went southwards to the Alps; the Visigoths conquered Rome and went on to southern France and Spain; and the Franks occupied Gaul.

It is interesting that Bronze Age burials in southern Siberia, in the Minussinsk district which is now the home of the nomadic Kirghiz and Kalmuck tribes, are skeletally of 'Nordic' type. The predominant physical type in this area only changed to Mongoloid during the 4th century. The early Slavs, who occupied the country to the east of the Celts and Germans, were also Nordic skeletally and according to literary descriptions they were tall and blond. Slav skeletons dating from the 8th to 11th centuries A.D. from Poland, Germany, Bohemia, Austria and

Russia have long heads and there is little if any trace of the brachycephaly considered typically Slavic.

Celtic type

Skeletally, the Celtic Iron Age type is characteristically mesocephalic and low vaulted, with sloping forehead and prominent nose. Individuals in Ireland and Scotland sometimes described as 'Celtic', with dark hair and blue eyes, are not necessarily Celtic in the skeletal sense, but are often of the Atlanto-Mediterranean physical type.

The Celtic language—Q Celtic in Ireland and Scotland, P Celtic in Wales, Brittany and the rest of Europe—was introduced by Bronze Age invaders about 1800 B.C. As a cultural entity, however, the Celts did not gain cohesion until Iron Age (La Tène) times, about 500 B.C., in the region of south-western Germany. Their main expansion was westwards into Belgium, northern France and the British Isles. Celtic invaders into northern Italy, the Gauls, overthrew the Etruscans, and Roman descriptions say these barbarians were remarkable for their height, muscularity, fair skin and hair and blue eyes. Blondism, however, does not seem to have been characteristic of the Celts as a whole.

Celtic skulls are very variable, some being long and others round. The round-heads in particular have very large heads and are powerfully built. Celtic Iron Age burials in Britain contrast with those of the later Anglo-Saxons, particularly in the low sloping forehead of the former compared with the steep, high forehead of the Anglo-Saxons. Greek and Roman sculpture, such as the well-known 'Dying Gaul', shows a round-headed type with fairly short face; skeletal remains, however, show that the typical Celtic face was long in the upper part. The Celtic type persisted in England into recent times, as seen for instance in the plague pit skeletons of 1666 A.D. and it is still particularly common in Ireland and the Scottish Highlands.

(5) Alpine

The Alpines (Fig. 12) are concentrated along a line extending from France eastwards through the Alps and the Balkans, into Asia Minor and thence north-westwards into Russia. The Alpines have mixed a good deal with Nordics to the north and with Mediterraneans to the south. They are characterized by a broad and high head (c.i. averages 85), high curved occiput, vertical forehead, moderately to strongly developed brow-ridges, round face, broad nose with blobby tip, well-developed chin. The hair is generally medium to dark brown, sometimes blond, generally straight but sometimes wavy; beard and body hair are abundant. The build is sturdy rather than stocky and the average height is 165 cm. (5 ft 5 in.). The complexion is sallow, but is not as dark as in the Mediterranean Proper.

Coon (1939) regarded the Alpines as reduced survivors of the brachycephalic component in the Mesolithic population of France. He argued that France was a marginal area during Neolithic and Bronze Age times and that invasions of Medi-terranean peoples were less important here than in most European countries. The roundest heads of all—hyperbrachycephalic—are found in the Massif Central, which must certainly always have been a refuge area.

The brachycephalic component in Upper Palaeolithic and Mesolithic populations was, how-ever, very small. Even in Mesolithic times round-heads appear to be relatively scarce, except among the burials at Ofnet in Bavaria and on the Tagus river in Portugal. It would seem that the present Alpines are too numerous to be accounted for merely by regarding them as Palaeolithic (or even Mesolithic) survivors. Also their geographic loca-tion today makes it difficult to believe that they were not caught up and changed by the numerous Mediterranean migrations. Finally, the difference between a Frenchman and a Spaniard is so slight that they should surely both be regarded as Mediterranean; the fact that one has a rounder head than the other is only one difference among many resemblances.

Fig. 12. A round-headed Alpine from southern Albania.
Based on a photograph by Coon

The increase of brachycephalization in Europe in historic times has already been discussed (p. 16), a process which was certainly hastened by successive Mongol invasions. It may be significant that the Alpine type predominates today in many areas of Asian settlement in Europe.

The increased round-headedness among Czechs during the last thousand years is as follows:

9th century A.D. average c.i. 76
16th ,, ,, ,, ,, 80
18th ,, ,, ,, ,, 85

These changes, of course, involved not only the shape of the skull but also facial and nasal measurements.

In Germany, where mixture of practically every racial type took place during its complicated history, certain broad trends can be made out. The Alpine brachy-cephalics are concentrated in Bavaria, while the longest heads are found in the west, adjoining the relatively long-headed populations of Flanders and the Nether-lands. From north to south, there is a decrease in stature and in the incidence of blondism. In Switzerland too the rounder-headed and darker people are in the south and east. Considerable Alpine as well as Dinaric elements also occur in northern Italy, and even some skulls from Pompeii are of Alpine type.

(6) East Baltic

The blond, round-headed inhabitants of north-eastern and eastern Europe may be grouped broadly as the East Baltics (Plate I). These people carried Finno-Ugrian languages of the Uralic linguistic stock to Europe.

The early nomads of the plains of central Asia were European in type, not Mongoloid. During their migrations, the Mongoloid Turks and Tatars gathered followers of this old Asiatic 'Nordic' type, as well as people with Armenoid or Dinaric features. These varied types invaded Russia before the Slavs began their eastward expansion and must have influenced the appearance of the present East Baltic people. The Magyars, who migrated to Hungary during the 9th and 10th centuries A.D., were Ugrians from the region between the Volga and the Urals and had some Turkish admixture. Skulls of these Magyar invaders are similar to those of the early Finns, which are generally mesocephalic.

The people generally grouped as East Baltics include the Finns, Poles, Estho-nians, Latvians, Livonians, Lithuanians and many Russians. The type is also common in Scandinavia and north-east Germany, where the term 'square-heads' was coined to describe the Junker type, often erroneously called 'Nordic' in pre-war Germany. The East Baltics differ from the Alpines in having a flatter occipital region, a flatter and squarer face, a more concave nose and rounded chin. The straight hair is the fairest of any group in the world and the eyes are light blue or grey. Shovel-shaped incisors are sometimes found among East Baltics.

(7) The Lapps

The Lapps live in the forested highlands of Sweden, the Norwegian coastal provinces of Trons and Finmark, the tundra of northern Finland and the Kola peninsula. Most of this territory is shared with Finns and Norwegians. The Reindeer Lapps live a nomadic life mainly in the forest and mountains, while the Sedentary Lapps settle along the coasts and rivers, where the main occupation is fishing.

Fig. 13. The Lapps are typically short and broad, a body-build adapted to a cold climate.

Based on a photograph

The skull is brachycephalic (c.i. averages 84), the forehead bulbous, narrow and steep, brow-ridges generally lacking, face very short and fairly broad, feeble development of the jaws and small teeth. The cheek-bones tend to project, but are not so exaggerated as the flaring Mongoloid malars. The nose is moderately broad, with concave bridge and snub tip. The eyes are generally dark brown, but are often light, and widely separated, set in low orbits. The hair is usually dark brown, thick, fine and straight, but is sometimes blond. Stature is short, averaging

159 cm. (5 ft. 3 in.), and the legs are very short in relation to the trunk (Fig. 13). The arms are rather long, hands and feet are small.

The Lapps are probably not closely related to the present Mongoloids but their ancestors were presumably 'archaic White', representing a stage in the evolution of both Caucasoid and Mongoloid stocks. It is likely that they evolved in western Siberia in the region of the Urals. Their language is an archaic variety of Finnic.

Their blood-group characters are highly individual; there is an Asiatic tendency in the frequencies for the rhesus series and the Duffy group, as well as in the tasting of PTC, but the A B O and M N S distributions are not typically Asiatic. The frequency of gene A is more than 30% and of gene A_2 35%, more than three times higher than the highest of any other population (in Europe generally, the frequency of A_2 is about 5%). The incidence of B is very low, almost as low as among the Basques. The frequency of M is the lowest in Europe and NS is higher than in any other population except the Ainu. Of the rhesus series, cDE is unusually high. The frequency of the haptoglobin gene Hp^1 is very low compared with other Europeans but somewhat higher than in most Asiatic populations (p. 41).

Caucasoids in India

The inhabitants of India are predominantly Mediterranean in origin; this is obvious from their resemblance to such people as the Arabs, and is clear from the appearance of European/Indian crosses, who are indistinguishable from the Mediterranean Proper type except that the skin may be slightly darker. Survivors of earlier, non-Mediterranean people are still found in the hills and jungles of central and southern India; these include the Veddoids and are described with the Australoid stock (p. 85).

The great confusion which has existed over racial classification in India has been caused largely by trying to tie in physical types with language groups (Fig. 14). The terms Aryan and Dravidian are purely linguistic and each of these language groups is spoken by several very different kinds of people. The original languages of the aboriginal inhabitants of India have been lost; Dravidian languages were adopted mainly in the south, while Aryan (Indo-European) speech came in from the north. There are also other linguistic groups, such as the partly Mongoloid Munda-speakers (Austronesian linguistic family). It is most confusing

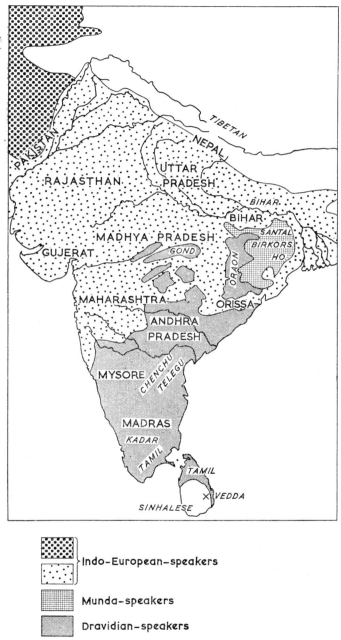

Fig. 14. Simplified distribution map of the peoples of India and Pakistan.

to classify the people of India as Pre-Dravidians, Dravidians or Indo-Europeans, as is usually done in anthropological text-books.

Apart from the Veddoids—descendants of the aboriginal inhabitants—the rest of the population of the sub-continent may be called quite simply Indians, whether descended from Dravidian-speakers or Aryan-speakers. These Indians are all of Mediterranean affinities, except for certain Mongoloids of the Himalayan region (see Plate VI). Within this group of Indians, two variants may be distinguished, a southern group and the main group, as well as the Irano-Afghan type in the north-west—a type which is seen typically in the Pathans and Sikhs, tall, heavily built people with strong beards.

(8) Southern Group

The darker-skinned agricultural populations of southern India who also spread into Ceylon, such as the Tamil (Plate V, left) and Telegu. This type was named 'Melanid' by Eickstedt (1934) and is sometimes referred to as 'Dravidian'; but although these people speak Dravidian languages, so do others of the Veddoid group in southern India. Physically, these 'Melanids' are fully Caucasoid, not Veddoid, although their dark skins give them a superficial resemblance to some of the Veddoid tribes.

(9) 'Mediterranean' Indians

The lighter-skinned, lightly built, long-headed, typically Mediterranean populations, termed 'Indid' by Eickstedt, form by far the largest group in India (Fig. 15). Within this group are innumerable castes, with the priestly Brahmins at the top. Both the Brahmins and the warrior Rajputs are believed to be near to the physical type of the Aryans. They are of medium stature, with small face, slightly developed chin, black and moderately wavy hair. Their languages are Indo-European (Aryan), but a few of the Veddoids of central India also speak languages of this stock.

In order to sort out this question of Dravidians and Aryans, it is necessary to go briefly into the history of India so far as it is known (which is not very far).

The advent of the Aryan-speakers in the north-west of the Indian sub-continent has been dated to about 1500 B.C. These barbaric nomads, who had little use for city life, are presumed to have destroyed the cities of the Indus valley copper-using civilization, which extended over nearly half a million square miles during the 2nd and 3rd millennia B.C. Skeletons from Mohenjo-daro (Sind) and Harappa (Punjab) include representatives of the aboriginal stock as well as long-headed Mediterraneans, who probably came from the area of Mesopotamia. At Mohenjo-daro there is evidence of a massacre, which is attributed to the Aryan invaders. For the next 500 years or so, little archaeological evidence has been found. But from about 1000 to 500 B.C. a Bronze Age culture suggests links with Iran and the Caucasus and is presumed to be associated with Aryan-speakers. These movements probably brought the tall, heavily built physical type into the north-west (Pakistan).

The origin of the speakers of the Dravidian languages, who consolidated themselves further south, is still completely unknown. The orthodox view is that they were already in India at the time of the Aryan invasions. Von Fürer-Haimendorf (1953), however, believed that the Dravidians may have entered India somewhat later than the Aryan-speakers, possibly arriving by sea or migrating by land along the west coast, though he does not even guess where they might have come from. Archaeological evidence has shown that about the middle of the first millennium B.C. an intrusive iron-using megalith-building civilization suddenly appeared in the Deccan and southern India. This civilization has been attributed tentatively to Dravidian-speaking invaders, though

Fig. 15. The Hindus are members of the far-flung Mediterranean Race.

After Dobzhansky

it may have been introduced by the Munda-speakers. Von Fürer-Haimendorf argued that the close integration and compactness of the Dravidian language group fits the assumption of a comparatively recent Dravidian expansion, beginning perhaps about 500 B.C. Allchin (1960), on the other hand, considers that 'it is now wellnigh impossible to envisage a Dravidian-speaking invasion of the South at so recent a date'. Future excavations may one day solve the Dravidian mystery; the key to it may well be the Brahuis, aborigines of Baluchistan, who speak a Dravidian language (Coon, *in lit.*).

Caucasoids in Africa

The Hamitic- and Semitic-speaking Mediterranean peoples of north and north-eastern Africa may be divided into two groups, Northern and Eastern; the Eastern group has varying degrees of Negroid admixture. It includes the ancient Egyptians, who were responsible for the greatest civilizations of Africa. Possibly their ancestors may have originated in western Asia; if so, some of them may have migrated to East Africa before the end of the Pleistocene, for skeletons of Mediterranean type appear in the Mesolithic of Kenya before any Negroid traits are recognizable. The term 'Hamite' (which strictly speaking is purely a linguistic term) has been loosely applied to a presumed non-Negroid racial stock south of the Sahara. Evidence suggests that these people may have spread as far as South Africa in early times and perhaps featured in the ancestry of the Hottentots. Moreover, there are varying amounts of 'Hamitic' blood in many of the Negroids with the exception of the Negroes of West Africa.

(10) Northern Group

The Northern group of Hamitic-speakers (the language is known as Libyco-Berber) comprises the Berbers of Cyrenaica, Tripolitania, Tunisia and Algeria (the 'Libyans') as well as the Berbers of Morocco; and the Tuareg and Tibu of the Sahara. The extinct Guanches of the Canary Islands also belonged to this family. The Berbers are the oldest surviving inhabitants of North Africa and many of them have an element of the Upper Palaeolithic Afalou type in their make-up, as well as the Neolithic Atlanto-Mediterranean type. Ancient Egyptian paintings sometimes show Libyans with light skin and fair hair, and the brow-ridges are often prominent.

　　The early history of North Africa is marked by a succession of invasions of Hamitic-speaking nomads from western Asia into territory occupied by agriculturalists of Neolithic tradition. Herodotus mentions descendants of Persians in North Africa and these people probably introduced the horse and chariot. Terrace cultivation with irrigation was probably diffused from the Yemen. The Zenata, who appeared in Roman North Africa during the 3rd and 4th centuries A.D., introduced the camel which enabled the Tuareg to settle in the Sahara. European influence—Greek, Phoenician and Roman—ceased with the advent of Islam in the 7th century and was not felt again until Napoleon's conquest of Algeria. There were two main waves of Arab invasions: the first from Arabia itself, soon after the death of the Prophet; and a second and larger invasion during the 11th century by Bedouin tribes from the Syrian desert. As a result of these invasions, many Berber groups were driven into the Sahara, where they displaced or subjugated the indigenous Negroes. Many of the Berbers have acquired Negroid blood through mixing with slaves from the Volta region, though some groups have remained relatively pure. The Arabs in North Africa are even more mixed with Negroes than are the Berbers and in general it is impossible to make clear-cut distinctions, on either cultural or physical grounds, between the Berber-speakers and the Arab-speakers.

Fig. 16. A Berber from Siwa; the Berbers are members of the group known as Northern Hamites.

Based on a Shell photograph

In Tunisia and Algeria, the mountain Berbers are terrace agriculturalists, while the Arabic-speakers of the plains and plateaux are mainly pastoralists. The mountain Berbers include the Shawia of the Aures mountains and Kabyles of the coastal region east of Algiers. In skeletal and skull measurements, these people (Fig. 16) are almost identical with the Nordics, though blond colouring is rare. It is among the Riffians of Morocco that blondism is such a striking feature; the skin is often pinkish-white, freckles are not uncommon, and the eyes are commonly mixed or light greenish-brown. The hair is wavy to curly, sometimes black, generally some shade of brown, occasionally reddish-brown; the beard is usually much

lighter than the head hair and is often reddish. Blood-group frequencies of the
Berbers of the Great Atlas are characterized by a high incidence of the rhesus
negative gene and low frequencies of the A and B groups. This suggests possible
connections with the Basques, a hypothesis which is supported by some linguistic
evidence. The southern group of Moroccan Berbers includes the Berbers of the
Middle Atlas, a group of Senhaja tribes which are part pastoralists, part agriculturalists. They are very tall people, with long face and convex nose.

The nomadic Tuareg roam over a vast territory of the Sahara and, although
they are Berbers, they are by no means typical of this group. The Tuareg noble
class has largely preserved its identity in spite of close proximity to Negroids.
These nobles are fairly tall, average stature 174 cm., lean, with long limbs,
narrow shoulders and hips, very long and narrow hands and feet. The head is large
and dolichocephalic, the face long and moderately broad, with high narrow forehead, high-bridged narrow nose with depressed tip. In pure nobles, skin colour is
brunet white, though those with only a minor degree of Negroid admixture are
dark brown. The Tibu of Tibesti merge into the Negroids of the central Sudan in
the south; those of the north are similar to the Berbers.

The 'Neolithic' inhabitants of the Canary Islands at the time of the Spanish
conquest had been isolated from the mainland for perhaps two thousand years
owing to lack of boats. They included tall, blond pastoralists and a darker type
which was generally associated with agriculture. The true 'Guanche' skulls are
very similar to the Afalou Upper Palaeolithic skulls, with strongly marked brow-
ridges. Although the Spaniards were struck by the blondism of the Guanches, as
well as their tall stature, it is likely that both these features were exaggerated;
stature calculated from their long bones is mainly medium and blond hair among
Guanche mummies is not common. The present inhabitants of these islands probably have at least as much Guanche blood as Spanish.

(11) Eastern Group

The Eastern group of Mediterraneans in Africa, sometimes called the Erythriotes,
comprises the Egyptians, the Beja from the Red Sea area, most of the inhabitants
of Ethiopia such as the Amhara, the Galla, Somali and Danakil, and the Berberine
or Nubians. They speak both Semitic and Hamitic languages; Semitic languages
were introduced from the Hadhramaut a few centuries before the Christian era
and are spoken by the Amharas, while others of the Eastern group are Hamitic-
speakers. The three main linguistic families of Hamitic are Berber and Chadic in

North Africa; ancient Egyptian and its derivative Coptic; and Cushitic—the linguistic group of East Africa.

All these people are predominantly Mediterranean, with Negroid admixture in varying degrees. The Negroid strain is greatest among the Sidamos, a group of agricultural peoples in the Galla country of south-western Ethiopia, and is least apparent in the Somali. The body build of all the peoples of this group is typically Mediterranean in the ratio of limbs and trunk; but the extremely long legs of the Somali find a close parallel in the Australians. The Somali are, in fact, exceptional in their very narrow face and jaws, dolichocephalic skull, straight 'European'-looking nose, characteristic chocolate brown skin colour, very narrow hips, small and delicate hands and feet. The Galla, who invaded southern Ethiopia in the 16th century, are similar in appearance to the Somali. They are mainly agricultural, though some are pastoral such as the nomadic Boran and Rendille of northern Kenya. The Afar (Danakil), who live on the Red Sea coast south of the Beja and north of the Galla and Somali, are lighter-skinned than the latter but otherwise similar.

The Semitic-speaking Amharas, and the Tigres who speak a parallel derivative of Ge'ez, vary enormously in skin colour, from light brown to black. They include a type with very light skin, high sloping forehead, very frizzy hair, and nose with a depressed tip, which is remarkably like the Papuans. The proportion of Negroid frizzy hair among the various groups varies from 70% among the Galla, 60% in the Amharas, to only 14% in the Somali. There has been so much infiltration of Negroes into Ethiopia through the slave trade that no area is free from admixture, though a few rare individuals show no visible signs of Negroid blood. Negroid traits, although apparent in the surface features, seldom appear in measurements of the skeleton, which show typically Mediterranean proportions.

The nomadic Beja tribes of the desert east of the Nile speak Cushitic languages. They include the Ababda, Bisharin, Hadendoa and Beni Amer. Some, such as the Haddendoa or 'Fuzzy Wuzzies' (Plate XI), are largely mixed with Sudanese Negroes. The least mixed resemble the predynastic Egyptians very closely. Skin colour is reddish-brown to dark brown, the nose is narrow and the lips thin.

The Egyptians, from predynastic to Roman times, were Mediterraneans of medium stature and with long heads; the ruling classes were often delicately built, like the modern Somali. A great variety of different peoples have infiltrated into Egypt in historical times, including Jews and Greeks in the Delta region and particularly into Alexandria; a flood of Arabs from the 7th century A.D. onwards;

next came the Turks, to Cairo and other cities; finally, countless Negroes and Abyssinians captured as slaves also mixed with the local population. The fellahin, however, are still very like the peasants of ancient Egypt, while the Copts have also remained near to the original type. Both fellahin and Copts vary from a narrow-faced, slender-jawed, hook-nosed form to a broader-faced type with strong jaws, prominent chin and a straight or concave nose. This heavier type first appeared during the time when the great pyramids were being built (around 2,500 B.C.). Average stature for the whole male population of Egypt is about 166 cm. (5 ft. 6½ in.), the skull is dolichocephalic (c.i. 74·5) and the nose mesor-rhine. Skin colour becomes progressively darker southwards, from a yellowish brunet in the Delta to medium brown in the Upper Nile region. Hair is generally curly, but varies from nearly straight to tightly spiralled; the colour is black or very dark brown.

The Nubians or Berberine are tall and lightly built. They have a darker skin and narrower face than the fellahin and are probably the result of mixture between Egyptian, Beja and Negroid peoples.

People from the Horn of Africa are believed to have invaded Uganda, Rwanda and Burundi a thousand years ago. Presumably they were quicker-witted and better armed than the indigenous Negroids, whom they reduced to the status of serfs, remaining themselves as a pastoral artistocracy. In Ankole (Uganda) this aristocracy is known as the Hima, in Rwanda as the Tutsi (most of them are now refugees in Uganda). The Tutsi, together with some of the Nilotic Negroids (p. 119), are the tallest people in the world; the men average 176 cm. (5 ft. 10 in.) in height and often exceed 195 cm. (6 ft. 6 in.). Their lives centre round their cattle, which they do not kill for meat but live mainly on milk and honey, together with beans and potatoes grown by their Bantu serfs, the Hutu. The Tutsi are able to leap to immense heights and are famous for their dancing. They are usually classified as 'Hamitic' (Caucasoid) but there is certainly a good deal of Negroid in their make-up and they speak a Bantu language.

VII

Australoids and Pacific Islanders

The Australoid stock is sometimes described as 'archaic White'. The evidence from skeletal remains, the distribution of the living representatives of this stock in peripheral areas, and the primitive-looking physical features all suggest a great antiquity for the Australoids. So-called 'primitive' features of the Australian aborigines, for instance, include prominent brow-ridges, receding forehead and chin, relatively low cranial capacity and large palate and teeth.

A generalized 'archaic White' was, so far as we know, the earliest form of *Homo sapiens*; many characteristics of the present Australoids are found in fossil human remains dating from the Upper Pleistocene. It seems most reasonable to suppose that the first 'archaic Whites' had light brown skin, dark hair and dark eyes and that subsequent variations towards both darker and lighter pigmentation arose as the result of mutations. Wavy hair predominates among the present Australoids and probably represents the ancestral form. Caucasoids and Australoids are the most primitive of the four major divisions of mankind in the retention of abundant facial and body hair.

Presumably owing to its greater antiquity, the White stock has differentiated more than the Mongoloids and Negroids. Another reason for this diversity may be that the Whites are less specialized than the other two, who are adapted for cold and hot conditions respectively.

Relics of the 'archaic White' stock still surviving today in Asia and Oceania are known as Australoids, to avoid confusion with the more progressive Whites or Caucasoids. They have diverged into two main branches: a gerontomorphic or rugged type, represented by the Australian aborigines, the Ainu and the Melanesians; and a lightly built pedomorphic type, represented by the Veddoids of India and Ceylon and by the extinct Tasmanians. A component of the rugged type is also found in the Polynesians and in the American Indians, both of whom are considerably mixed with Mongoloid (the Polynesians are perhaps predominantly 'archaic White', while the American Indians are certainly mainly Mongoloid).

F

81

1. Australian Aborigines

Of all the living races of man, the Australian aborigines are nearest to the specialized races of the Upper Pleistocene, such as Solo Man and Rhodesian Man (see Fig. 5). Their Mesolithic culture was (and still is in remote areas) without pottery, agriculture or metals when they first came into contact with Europeans. They must have originated somewhere in south-eastern Asia and probably reached Australia late in Pleistocene times via New Guinea, which was then joined to Asia. A skull from Keilor near Melbourne was found in a flood deposit, which in its upper part contained charcoal dated by radiocarbon to about 6,500 B.C. It differs from skulls of modern aborigines only in its larger cranial capacity.

The belief that the Australian aborigine is dominantly 'White', but of an archaic type, is supported by the fact that in Australian/Caucasoid crosses the hybrid loses most of the 'primitive' characters, as well as the darker skin colour; whereas in Australian/Mongoloid hybrids the Mongoloid traits are more in evidence than the Australoid traits. The dark pigmentation, as well as the broad nose, were perhaps acquired through mutations encouraged by natural selection in a tropical environment. Blood group B, so characteristic of Asia, is absent among the aborigines except in the extreme north and north-east, where its presence is attributed to admixture with Indonesians who are partly Papuan. The high incidence of group N among the Australians is characteristic also of the Melanesians and of the Ainu, which supports the view that all these people are related. The Melanesians, however, have a moderately high frequency of the gene S (of the M N S series) which the Australians lack. As far as the rhesus series is concerned, the most remarkable feature among the Australian aborigines is the relatively high frequency of the rare combination CDE, which is found also among the Veddoids.

Four types of Australian aborigines were distinguished by Birdsell (1949), the two main groups being the Murrayan and the Carpentarian. The Murrayan of the more temperate region of south-eastern Australia—the Murray River basin and Gippsland—was said to be more 'Caucasoid' and to be very like the Ainu. The Carpentarian type further north was said to have more of the Melanesian-Papuan element, and to resemble the Veddoids; the Carpentarians show adaptations to desert conditions in their darker skin and taller, more slender build. The third type, a blend between Murrayan and Carpentarian, was said to exist in the desert interior of the continent. Lastly, the Barrineans, a Negrito-like type with frizzy hair resembling the extinct Tasmanians, was distinguished in the rain forests of Queensland. Abbie (1951, 1958), however, does not recognize these four as distinctive types, but considers that they all grade into one another. He also believes that the Tasmanians arrived direct from Melanesia rather than from the mainland of Australia. The last Tasmanian died in 1876, but a few of mixed blood are left; the skulls of the Tasmanians are rounder and have a more infantile appearance than those of the Australians and are far more like those of Negritos. Their ancestors may perhaps be represented by a skull from Niah Cave in Sarawak, apparently dating from the Upper Pleistocene of some 40,000 years ago.

Typically, the Australian skull is long and narrow, with low retreating forehead and large brow-ridges, flattened nose and some prognathism; the mouth is very wide and the palate large. The mean cranial index for males is 70·2 (the cephalic index is about 2 points higher) but the range is from 64·2 to 75·3. Cranial capacities range from as little as 850 c.c. to more than 1,500 c.c. The jaws are not particularly massive, but the teeth are large, associated with alveolar prognathism. Skin colour darkens with exposure to the sun and tends to be darker in the north of the continent where heat and humidity are greater. Hair is normally dark brown or black, and although children with fair or reddish hair are not uncommon, their hair darkens considerably with age. Mean adult male stature is between 5 ft. 4 in. and 5 ft. 7 in. Leg length is more than half the total stature—quite different to the proportion found in Europeans and more like that of Negroes. The femur is long, with the tibia only slightly shorter. Hands and feet are long and slender. The trunk too is slender, with narrow shoulders and hips. The Murrayans tend to have a more stocky build, with shorter legs.

In spite of contacts with people with a Neolithic culture on islands to the north, agriculture, domesticated animals and pottery were never adopted by the Australians. They arrived with a Mesolothic phase of culture, in which they have remained until the present day. This fact, according to Abbie, argues against the successive waves of immigrants to Australia which have sometimes been postulated. The main stone implements of the aborigines include the hafted stone axe and knife, and microliths (tiny flakes of regular form) mounted as the barbs of spear-heads, teeth of saw-knives, and so on. Weapons consist of clubs, spears, spear-throwers and throwing-sticks, including the boomerang. Women use digging-sticks to uproot yams and other roots. Coastal aborigines use spears, nets and lines for fishing and they make rafts and canoes from bark or logs. The dog, which the aborigines brought with them when they first immigrated to Australia, is used to help in hunting.

Two hundred years ago, when Europeans first arrived in Australia, there may have been some 300,000 aborigines, grouped in bands of up to 500. The Australians formed the largest and most isolated group of pre-agricultural Stone Age people left in the world. But the population was decimated by European diseases. Resistance was greatly reduced by the psychological factor of despair at the disparity between their own culture and that of the Europeans. Now only about 70,000 remain in the Reserves, of whom some two-thirds are pure bred. In the main, each tribe has its own language and contact with others is made by signs. Aboriginal rock paintings (see frontispiece) and carvings, dances and music, as well as the practice of making strange sounds with the bullroarer and *churinga*, may well have remained unchanged for thousands of years.

2. Ainu

The 'hairy Ainu' (Fig. 17), whose ancestors can be traced to the Stone Age inhabitants of Japan, were pushed into the cold northerly islands of Hokkaido and Sakhalin by the arrival of Mongoloids. They are clearly a branch of the archaic White stock, which was once widespread in Asia and also probably in Europe. Recent Mongoloid admixture is often seen, however, and is especially noticeable in females.

Fig. 17. An Ainu from Hokkaido, member of the archaic White stock.
Based on a photograph by Kohama

The Ainu skull is similar to that of the Australian, though it is generally mesocephalic rather than dolichocephalic and the chin is far more pronounced. The body build is thickset, with long arms and short legs, and the average stature is low. The skin is brownish or greyish white. The men are characterized by the heaviest growth of facial and body hair to be found in any living population. Often the Ainu show a striking resemblance to Russian peasants, and it seems quite probable that the ancestral White stock once extended right across Asia into Russia. The Ainu were great hunters of bear and deer; they also depended largely on fishing, and trained dogs to round-up the fish. Like some of the Upper Palaeolithic peoples of Europe, they had bear ceremonies; a bear cub was tamed and finally sacrificed so that it might convey messages to the gods.

Although the Ainu resemble the Australians in having blood group N in excess of M, the frequency of the gene S suggests closer relationship with inhabitants of the Marshall Islands in north-eastern Micronesia.

3. Veddoids

The Veddoids of the hills and jungles of central and southern India are the most ancient and primitive inhabitants of the sub-continent. In former times, their territory must have extended over most of India; but they were driven into refuge areas by advancing pastoralists and agriculturalists—Aryan-speakers from the north, Dravidian-speakers from the south—during the 2nd and 1st millennia B.C.

The Veddoids are short, average stature 157 c.m., skin colour is chocolate brown, hair very wavy or curly, body hair scanty (although some men develop moderate beards). The head is very long and relatively small. The general appearance of the face is round and child-like. The chin is slightly developed, the forehead rather sloping, and often bulbous, and the brow-ridges often quite strongly developed. They often have a rather broad snub nose and the lips are full and curved. Some facial prognathism is often present.

Eickstedt (1934) distinguished two types of Veddoids in India. The more primitive, darker-skinned group is found mainly in the mountains of the south from the Cardamon hills to the Nilgiri and includes hunting and food-gathering tribes such as the Chenchu of Andhra Pradesh and the Kadar of Kerela. The larger group in central India includes primitive agriculturalists like the Gond tribes of Madhya Pradesh and the Oraons of Chota Nagpur. On the whole these people are taller, with rather lighter skin, somewhat longer face and narrower nose than the Veddoids of the south. Coon (1958) regards all these people as Australoid, but not 'Veddoid'—a term which he restricts to 'small, primitive Caucasoids' such as the Birhors of Chota Nagpur.

The Munda-speaking tribes of Chota Nagpur and other parts of the north-east are probably mainly Australoid, with Mongoloid admixture. Their languages are of the Austro-Asiatic group, quite distinctive from both Dravidian and Indo-European (see p. 72).

The Vedda of Ceylon (Fig. 18) are very similar to their kin on the mainland, though they are even smaller in stature. Very few pure Vedda remain—and they live only in the eastern part of the island—although their genes are probably widespread in Ceylon. At one time it was suspected that the Vedda might have a common ancestry with African negroes owing to the relatively high incidence of the sickle-cell trait in both, particularly when it was discovered that some

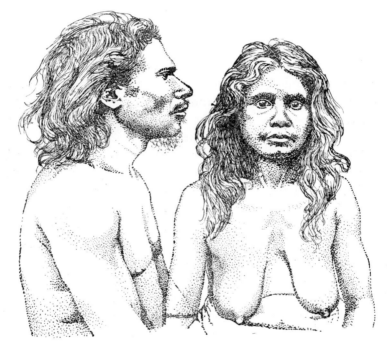

Fig. 18. The Vedda represent the oldest aboriginal population of India, some of whom migrated to Ceylon.

Based on a photograph by Sarasin

of the aboriginal inhabitants of intermediate areas such as the Hadhramaut also shared this characteristic. However, the trait probably increased by natural selection in response to similar malarial environments and it implies no relationship between Negroids and Veddoids. Another former hypothesis suggested connections between African Negrillos and an early Negrito strain in Asia, represented perhaps by the present Andaman islanders, but this theory also has now been abandoned by most authorities.

Early human remains are scarce in this part of the world, but skeletons of the so-called Balangoda people of Ceylon who were accompanied by a Mesolithic culture are said to be of Veddoid type and are taller than the present Vedda. No remains resembling Negritos have ever turned up in ancient deposits. The very dark skin and other so-called 'Negroid' characteristics of the Veddoids must be regarded as independent parallel mutations in climatically similar environments in Africa and India. In many ways some of the Veddoids resemble diminutive Australians—both in the form of the skull and in surface features such as the broad nose. The rare rhesus combination CDE has been found among some Veddoids as well as in Australians.

Other members of the Veddoid stock probably include the aboriginal inhabitants of the Hadhramaut and Dhofar and extensions of the same basic stock are found in the interior of some of the islands of Indonesia.

4, 5. Pacific Islanders

The Pacific islanders may be divided into two very different groups: the dark-skinned *Melanesians*, including the Papuans and the pygmy Negritos; and the light-skinned *Polynesians*, with their relations in Micronesia.

Racial classification of these peoples varies greatly with different authors. The first group used to be regarded as an eastern branch of the Negroid stock and it was also supposed that the Asiatic and Oceanic Negritos were related to the African Negrillos. However, blood-group frequencies are so entirely different in the two continents that it is very unlikely that the 'Oceanic Negroids' and the African Negroids are related. More probably the dark skin and frizzy hair were developed through independent mutations, encouraged by natural selection in similar tropical environments (see Plates III and XI). The very distinctive characteristics of the African Negroids are not fully developed in the Melanesians. Although their hair is frizzy it does not grow in the tiny spirals which produce 'woolly' hair. The lips are seldom so full and everted, the nose is not so broad, and there is less prognathaism, though these features are more pronounced in the Negritos than in the Papuans.

Skeletally the Melanesians and more particularly their ancestors the Palaeo-Melanesians (p. 89) must be grouped with the 'archaic White' stock, and the incidence of blood group N links them with the Australian aborigines.

The problem of the Polynesians is even more difficult. Ashley Montagu (1951) regarded them as a 'far-flung branch of the Mediterranean stock'; Trevor (1955) grouped them with the Mongoloids under the stock which he called Mongoliform. Coon *et al.* (1950) classified the Polynesians as a separate major stock. Hooton (1947) considered them to be a composite race, predominantly white. Probably

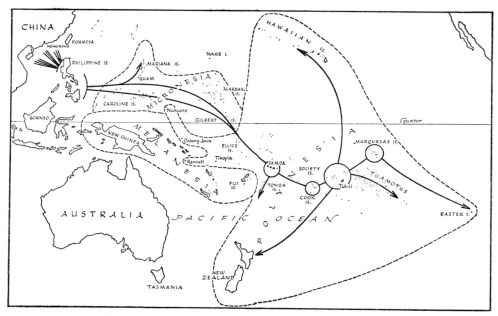

Fig. 19. Migration routes to Polynesia and Micronesia.

After Coon

the most acceptable explanation is that their ancestors were of the archaic White stock and mixed with later Mongoloids. They are, in fact a relatively new composite race.

4. Melanesians

The main islands in Melanesia are New Guinea and Fiji. Both the Papuans of New Guinea (Plate II) and the Fijians (Plate III, below; Fig. 20) must have emigrated from the mainland through the Malay peninsula and, indeed, skeletons of these 'Palaeo-Melanesians' have been found associated with Mesolithic industries in Malaya, Indochina, Sumatra and Java. The skull from Niah Cave in Borneo seems to represent a less gerontomorphic branch of this group. The

Palaeo-Melanesians bear certain resemblances to the Wadjak people, as well as to the Veddoids, but their closest link is with the present Papuans and New Caledonians (Tweedie, 1953). The most convincing explanation of the Negritos is that they are diminished survivors of this stock.

The Papuans are medium to rather tall in stature, averaging 168 cm. (5 ft. 7 in.). They have very dark chocolate brown skin, frizzy hair and characteristically a prominent nose with depressed tip. The head is usually fairly long, but some are also broad (that is to say altogether large). The forehead is sloping and brow-ridges are often well marked.

The Melanesians of Fiji, the Admiralty Islands, the Bismarck archipelago, the Solomons, Santa Cruz and the New Hebrides tend to be shorter than the Papuans, with longer head, rounded forehead, less prominent brow-ridges and broader nose. The Fijians are mixed with Polynesian strains.

Negritos survive in tropical forests in widely separated refuge areas. They include the Andamanese, the Semang of Malaya, the Aeta of Luzon, and various tribes in the interior of New Guinea and other islands in

Fig. 20. The dark skin and frizzy hair of the Melanesians give them a superficial resemblance to African negroes (see also Plates III and XI).

After Dobzhansky

Melanesia. They are all characterized by very low stature, dark skin, frizzy hair and an infantile appearance of the face.

The Andaman islanders speak a unique language and live mainly by fishing. Their average height is only 137 cm. (4 ft. 6 in.). They are of particular interest owing to their resemblance to the Bushmen of South Africa. Both these widely separated people share the unique combination of peppercorn hair and steatopygia (see Fig. 2 and Plate X). Blood-group evidence makes it unlikely that they are related so presumably this is another case of independent parallel mutations encouraged by natural selection. Among the Onge tribe of the Andamanese, the rhesus factor CDe has an incidence of 92%, which suggests connections with Melanesia. The Onges also have a frequency of more than 50% of blood group A, which is only equalled and surpassed among some groups of American Indians.

Taken as a whole, the blood-group evidence links the remote Andamanese of the Indian Ocean with the Negritos of Oceania.

Typical of the Oceanic Negritos are the pygmy inhabitants of the central range of New Guinea, whose existence was quite unsuspected until recently. They average 145 cm. (4 ft. 9 in.) in height; their skin colour is yellowish-brown; their hair is frizzy and rather abundant on face and body; while the nose is short, broad and flat.

5. Polynesians

Archaeological evidence, particularly radiocarbon dating, has recently provided some clues about the mysterious origins and relationships of the Polynesians. There are three theories as to how they reached the widely scattered islands of the Pacific (see Fig. 19):

(a) The older view was that their ancestors sailed from Indonesia.

(b) Thor Heyerdahl has postulated that they came in waves from the Americas.

(c) More recently it has been suggested that they originated in southern China, in the region of Canton and Hainan island, crossing to the Philippines and thence by way of Micronesia to Polynesia. Radiocarbon dates from Saipan in the Marianas suggest that seafarers reached Micronesia at a time when the Chinese were beginning to expand from the north into central and southern China. The Neolithic inhabitants of these regions were mainly pushed out into Siam, while others went to Indonesia *via* Hainan and the Philippines.

The Polynesian islands lie inside a triangle, with Tahiti in the middle, Hawaii at the top, Samoa and Tonga half-way down on the western side of the triangle, New Zealand in the bottom corner on the west, Easter Island in the bottom corner on the east (Fig. 19). Each side of this triangle measures about 5,000 miles. The immense distances between many of the islands necessitated skilled navigation, and this requirement explains why they were populated only at a relatively late date. It has been said that the longer voyages were accidental rather than deliberate; but recent excavations in Hawaii and in the Marquesas have revealed bones of domestic pigs and dogs in the earliest levels, implying large-scale expeditions fully equipped for settlement (Suggs, 1960). The oldest radiocarbon date obtained so far for Polynesia comes, surprisingly enough, from the Marquesas, a group of islands north-east of Tahiti and thus on the far eastern side of the tri-angle. Charcoal associated with human burials there has been dated to 2080 ± 150 years before the present, or about 130 B.C. (Shapiro & Suggs, 1959). The western borders of Polynesia were presumably occupied long before this (unless of course Heyerdahl's theory is correct, in which case the colonizers sailed from American shores). It has been estimated that Tahiti was inhabited at least by 550 B.C. From this central point, navigators sailed north to Hawaii (radiocarbon date of the earliest camp site here is A.D. 128 ± 200 years); eastwards to Easter Island (earliest recorded date A.D. 380 ± 100); and eventually south-westwards to New Zealand, where the moa-hunting ancestors of the Maoris had arrived by about A.D. 1125 (the earliest radiocarbon date obtained so far).

The radiocarbon dates obtained for the earliest settlement of Polynesia support other estimates arrived at by *glottochronology*. It has been found that language elements change at a rate of about 19% in every thousand years. Polynesian dialects differ from other Austranesian languages by 50%, which suggests that the Polynesians had been isolated in Oceania for about 2,000 years before Euro-peans arrived there (since then, of course, there have been rapid changes in the language).

The twin-hulled canoes which brought the first Polynesians to Hawaii must have been similar to the ones which Captain Cook saw in use some 1,300 years later. There are reports of canoes over 100 ft. long, which could carry 140 men. Captain Cook actually saw one 70 ft. long and 12 ft. broad. At the time of his discovery of the Hawaiian islands in 1778, the population numbered about 300,000. The people were in a Neolithic stage of culture, without metals or writing. A hundred years later the population had been reduced to 60,000 by disease and now there are only some 11,000 pure Hawaiians left, together with about 75,000 of part Hawaiian blood (Joesting, 1960).

The Polynesians are one of the tallest and finest-looking races in the world (see Plate III, top). The fact that they show great variability is attributed to their presumed composite origin. Their skin colour is usually yellowish-brown, but ranges from nearly white to dark brown; the head varies from dolichocephalic to brachycephalic; the face is generally long and narrow, but may be short and broad. A feature particularly common in Polynesians and very rare in other races is the 'rocker jaw', curved on the lower side so that it rocks when laid on a table; this character has been found in about half the Polynesians who have been studied. The hair in Polynesians is usually wavy, but is sometimes straight and occasionally frizzy. There are some individuals showing Mongoloid features (Plate VII, right), others are more Australoid like the Melanesians, others again resemble Europeans (Plate III, top). Birdsell's findings that crossings between Australian aborigines and Mongoloids produce hybrids very like the Polynesians is significant support for the theory that the Polynesians originated from archaic White and Mongoloid.

In their blood-group frequencies, the Polynesians and the North American Indians differ almost completely from all the other peoples of Asia and the Pacific. Thus, according to Mourant (1959), there can be little doubt that they have ancestors in common. Again, this bears out the theory of archaic White and Mongoloid ancestry in both these races.

VIII

Mongoloids (including American Indians)

The Mongoloids probably arose in north-eastern Asia from an archaic White or pre-Mongoloid stock, represented by the modern Ainu. The differentiation of the true Mongoloids may have been due to isolation and extreme specialization during the later part of the Ice Age, when these people were subjected to intense selection of characters aiding survival in extreme cold (p. 31). That some incipient Mongoloid characters had already developed before the end of the Upper Pleistocene is evident from the skulls found in the Tzeyang and in the Liukiang caves in Kwangsi, south-western China. Some of the later (Mesolithic) skulls from China, however, are non-Mongoloid (Chang, 1960), indicating the survival of the pre-Mongoloid stock into post-Pleistocene times.

Although Coon's theory that the Mongoloid face became moulded by 'climatic engineering' seems plausible, the effects of diet should not be overlooked and various other speculations about the origins of this stock have been made, some of them extremely questionable. One theory links the development of the Mongoloid type with thyroid deficiency, due to lack of iodine in areas far from the sea.

Another theory regards the Mongoloid as the result of foetalization—the retention of infantile characters in the adult. Races retaining the most infantile characters are considered to be the most advanced (in a physical, not a cultural, sense) and the latest to have evolved; this agrees with the supposition that the Mongoloid stock became differentiated relatively late. Such pedomorphic features include brachycephaly, lack of pronounced brow-ridges, presence of epicanthic folds, and absence of beard and body hair. This theory of foetalization could also account for the so-called 'Mongoloid' characters in the Bushmen (p. 24).

According to Coon's theory, the hardy Mongoloids, having been weeded out by rigorous natural selection, increased tremendously after the end of the Ice Age. When Neolithic agriculturalists from the west immigrated into China, they taught the nomadic Mongoloids to farm; the result of interbreeding was the swamping of Caucasoid characters by the dominant Mongoloid strain. Much later, farmers

93

invaded Indochina, Siam and Burma and thus Mongoloids, primarily adapted for the cold, were brought into a tropical environment. Some of their extreme specializations, such as the thickset body, short legs and layers of fat, were lost and replaced by the more graceful proportions of the Indonesian race. The flat face, however, remained; presumably this was because it has no selective disadvantage.

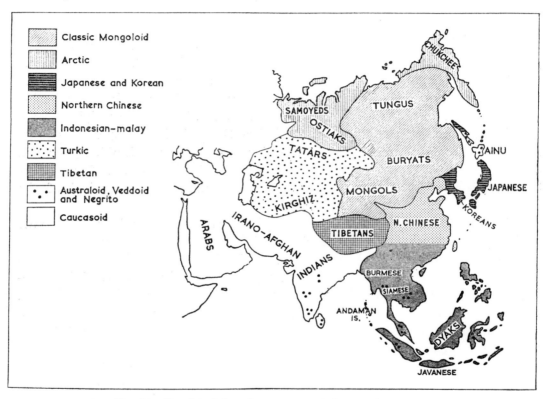

Fig. 21. Simplified distribution map of the peoples of Asia.

In the meantime, about 500 B.C., nomads from the west introduced horses to the Mongolian plains. The population increased tremendously and attacked the Chinese empire. The Chinese victory caused some of these invaders to fly westwards again—to the Volga basin and the grasslands of Europe.

Inevitably, owing to its geographical location, Asia occupies a central position also for racial movements. In the west, Mongoloids merge into Caucasoids with no clearly defined boundary between the two. From north-eastern Asia, the peopling of America took place; and from the south-east, there were migrations to Australia and the islands of the Pacific. Only in the south has the barrier of the Himalayas made a sharp dividing line between Mongoloids of the plateaux to the north and Caucasoids of the lowlands of India.

It is hardly necessary to repeat the characteristics of the Mongoloid stock. Briefly they are: yellowish skin; coarse, straight black hair; little beard or body hair; round head, high, flaring cheek-bones, little or no development of the brow-ridges; flat face and nose; internal epicanthic fold of the upper eyelid; and relatively little sexual dimorphism. Another characteristic, found in about 90% of Mongoloids including American Indians, is the presence of shovel-shaped incisors, i.e. these teeth are scooped out behind. This feature was already present in Peking Man four hundred thousand years ago and is occasionally found also in non-Mongoloid peoples. The so-called 'Mongol spot', a patch of darker pigment at the base of the spine, was formerly thought to be characteristic only of Mongoloid babies, but is now known to occur in infants of many races.

The Mongoloid stock may be divided into the following groups (see Fig. 21): Classic Mongoloids (including also the Eskimoid or Arctic type; the Japanese and Korean type; and the Northern Chinese type); the Turkic race; the Tibetan or Himalayan race; the large and widely scattered Indonesian-Malay race; and the American Indians.

1. Classic Mongoloid

The *Classic Mongoloids* show the features of extreme specialization for cold already described. They include such people as the Tungus (Plate IV, left), who range from the Arctic circle to 40° N. and from the Yenesei to the Pacific; the Ostyaks; and the Buryats of the Lake Baikal region. The Tungus have a rather longer head and face than the Buryats; they are very similar skeletally to Huns of the 3rd to 5th centuries A.D. from cemeteries in Hungary. A brachy-cephalic type, common in the somewhat later Avar cemeteries, may be compared with the Buryats. These successive waves of Mongoloid invaders introduced a completely new racial element into Europe.

The Samoyeds, who wander along the Arctic shores of Siberia and into Europe (where they border on the Lapps in the Kola peninsula), are predominantly of the Classic Mongoloid type but also show some Caucasoid features. They are muscular in build and very short. Skull measurements of Samoyeds and Lapps are comparable, but the Samoyed face is wider and the cheek-bones are more flaring. A few Samoyeds have light or mixed blue eyes and blond or medium brown hair. The Samoyeds are Uralic-speakers, though they arose in the region north of the Altai mountains now occupied by Altaic-speakers. Some of the fully Mongoloid Altaic-speakers extend also into Europe, for instance the Kalmucks.

Eskimoid or Arctic Type

The Eskimos (see Plate IV, right) and similar Arctic peoples such as the Reindeer and the Coastal Chukchee are clearly related closely to the Classic Mongoloids described above. The Eskimos of north-eastern Asia and North America have similar physical features, culture and language in the two continents. Moreover, the Eskimos are clearly distinctive from the American Indians; probably they arrived from Asia later than the other aboriginal inhabitants of the New World The occurrence of blood group B among the Eskimos, but not among American Indians, seems to support the archaeological evidence of a later migration of the Eskimos.

Eskimos are characterized by a large, broad face; brachycephalic or mesocephalic skull with a high, keeled vault; exaggeratedly flaring cheek-bones; high incidence of the complete epicanthic eye-fold; short legs, small hands and feet, and thick trunk. Apart from shovel-shaped incisors—which are found also among other Mongoloid peoples—the Greenland Eskimos have certain peculiarities of the teeth which include large pulp cavities and fused roots. The jaws are extremely strong and powerful; they are constantly exercised in chewing tough meat, skins and even boots (to keep them soft). Asiatic, Aleutian and Alaskan Eskimos are brachycephalic and short, average stature 152 cm. (about 5 ft. 1 in.); the Greenland Eskimo is somewhat taller, average 155 cm. (5 ft. 2 in.), and mesocephalic.

The word 'Eskimo' means 'eaters of raw meat' and was first applied to these people by certain American Indian tribes. The Eskimos' own word for themselves is *Inuit*, meaning 'people'. Along the whole length of Eskimo territory from the Bering Straits to eastern Greenland—a distance of about 3,400 miles—the dialects are remarkably similar; this supports the archaeological evidence that the Eskimos are relative newcomers to North America. It has been calculated that the first Aleuts, speaking a proto-Eskimo language, reached the Aleutian Islands about 3,000 years ago. The Aleuts mummified their dead and travelled immense distances in their *bidarkas* (the equivalent of the Eskimo *kayak*) in pursuit of whales, which they killed with poisoned spear-heads. With his *kayak*, his harpoon, and his igloo, the Eskimo is perfectly adapted to his harsh environment and is one of the most cheerful people in the world.

Japanese and Korean Type

In general, the Japanese are rather short and robustly built. The face is broad, the eyes slanting, the nose flat and the mouth rather wide. A finer type is found among the upper classes; such people are taller and slimmer, with a somewhat longer head and narrower, straight or convex nose. Some of the men have straight eyes, but those of the women are nearly always slanting. The main difference between the Japanese and the Koreans is that the former have more facial and body hair and are usually taller.

Many anthropologists have classified the Japanese with the Malay branch of the Indonesian-Malay race. Coon *et. al* (1950), however, grouped the Japanese and Koreans with the Classic Mongoloids. Most of their features are indeed similar, particularly the flat face, epicanthic fold, coarse straight hair, and small extremities.

Fig. 22. A typical Mongol.

Based on a photograph by Coon

G

Northern Chinese Type

There is a marked difference between the Northern and Southern Chinese (who are of Indonesian type). The north was invaded by waves of Tungus, Mongols (Fig. 22) and Manchus, all of whom left their mark on the population. These invasions also resulted in innumerable dialects and the need for some sort of *lingua franca* caused the adoption of common signs in the written language.

The Northern Chinese are considerably taller and more slenderly built than those of the south. The forehead is inclined to be retreating and there is a marked constriction at the level of the temples.

2. Turkic

The pastoralists and agriculturalists of central Asia are mixed with Caucasoid strains. They include three branches of Altaic-speakers: an eastern branch in East Turkestan; a central branch consisting of the Kirghiz of the mountains of Tienchan and the Pamirs, as well as the Tatars of the Volga and the Caucasus;

Fig. 23. A Tibetan. Like many of the American Indians, the Tibetans show an admixture of Mongoloid and archaic White strains (compare with Fig. 26).

Based on a photograph by Coon

and a western branch comprising the Turkomans of Iran and Russian Turkestan and the Aderbaidjani (Turkicized Iranians).

Body build is rather robust, face very broad, nose and cheek-bones prominent, head round, beard often abundant. The eyes are non-Mongoloid, but often have an external fold; the lips are usually rather thick (see Plate I, below).

3. Tibetan or Himalayan

The mountain people of Tibet (Fig. 23), Nepal (Plate VI, left), Sze-Chuan and northern Burma appear to be the result of mixture between the archaic White stock and fully evolved Mongoloids. The Tibetan face is narrower than that of the Classic Mongoloid and is less padded with fat, while the nose is typically prominent, resembling that of some American Indians.

An interesting and little-known people belonging to this race are the Lolos, who live near the headwaters of the Yangtze between China, Tibet and Burma. Their skin is brown and the eyes are seldom of the extreme Mongoloid form. The men are strong and muscular and they are brave warriors.

4. Indonesian-Malay

The people of south-eastern Asia are grouped in the Indonesian-Malay race (the terms Indonesian and Malaysian are not, of course, used in the political sense here); they include the southern Chinese, Thai, Burmese, Filipinos and many others. Indonesians, mixed with Negroids, are also found in Madagascar, where Mongoloid features are strongest in the interior of the island. The ancestors of the Malagasy may have reached Madagascar about the 1st century A.D.

The Indonesian type is slender and short. The head is mesocephalic (average c.i. $78 \cdot 5$); the nose is narrower and higher than in the Malay type and the epicanthic fold occurs less frequently. Many of the people of southern China, Burma, Borneo (Fig. 24), Thailand and nearly the whole of the former Indo-China are classed as Indonesians; the Cambodians, however, are a relatively tall people of Malay type. The Cambodians occupied a large area before the arrival of the shorter and more Mongoloid-looking Annamese, who invaded Indo-China at about the same time as the Burmese. The last to arrive were the Thai, who came from the region of Sechuan. The Thais include the Thos and Muong in the north-east,

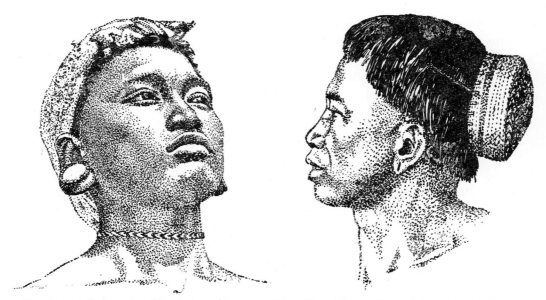

Fig. 24. An Indonesian (Iban) from Borneo.   Fig. 25. A Malay (Bontoc) from the Philippines.
Based on a photograph by Shell   *Based on a photograph by Shell*

the Shans in the north-west, the Laotians in the south-east, and the Siamese in the south-west. The Siamese are characteristically very round-headed, with prominent cheek-bones, a short, flat nose and olive skin; they are an admixture of Indonesian and Malayan types.

The people of Malaya and the Philippines (Fig. 25) are rather taller than the Indonesians, averaging 158 cm. (5 ft. 3 in.), and the hair is straight rather than slightly wavy. In general, Mongoloid characters are more marked than in the Indonesian type. In the Malay archipelago, the Malay type predominates near the coasts, while the Indonesian type occurs mainly in the interior of the islands. The population of Sarawak, North Borneo, consists of the Sea Dyaks, a war-like people living on the coast, and the peaceful Land Dyaks who live in communal long-houses; they are rather strongly built people, with features very similar to the Polynesians.

5. American Indian

The undoubted Mongoloid ancestry of the American Indians is not always particularly apparent from their appearance. A person knowing nothing about anthropology might well think that a 'Redskin' is about as different from a Chinaman as he could possibly be; almost all they seem to have in common is straight, coarse black hair. But it is only the hook-nosed Plains Indians who are commonly pictured (Fig. 26); and, although these are so much better-known, they are by no means typical of the inhabitants of the New World as a whole. The agricultural tribes of the south-west and South America have a far more Mongoloid appearance (see Plates VI and VII).

Fig. 26. A Plains Indian of North America.
After Dobzhansky

Compared with Asiatics, skin colour of the Amerindians is darker and sometimes more reddish than yellow; the nose may be hooked or straight, sometimes concave, but very rarely flat as in the typical Mongoloid. The brow-ridges are often well developed, while the Mongoloid forehead is typically smooth. The complete Mongoloid eye-fold does not occur among American Indians and the inner epicanthic fold is uncommon in men, although it appears more frequently among women and children.

Archaeological evidence makes it clear that man reached the New World towards the end of the last glacial period, probably between 20,000 and 10,000 years ago, via the Bering Straits. This date has been established mainly from finds of Folsom and other fluted stone points in the south-west associated with bones of extinct species of bison and other animals. A radiocarbon date of $10,780 \pm 375$ years before the present was announced in 1960 for a Folsom site in Colorado.

The first of the immigrants to America were probably of the archaic White stock similar to the people of the Upper Cave at Choukoutien and other Late Pleistocene sites in China. Representatives of this type have been recognized in the Cahuilla and Pomo tribes of California (Birdsell *in* Laughlin, 1951). Skulls from the lowest levels of excavations in early American Indian sites are mostly dolichocephalic, for instance those from Lagoa Santa in eastern Brazil, while the round-heads are usually associated with higher levels. An apparent exception is the brachycephalic skull from Tepexpan, Mexico, associated with bones of extinct elephant and provisionally dated to about 9000 B.C. The round-heads as a whole seem to represent Mongoloid immigrants who arrived from about 6000 B.C. onwards. These people worked their way down the west coast, spreading eastwards from the Rockies and from the Andes; eventually they were responsible for the highest developments of American civilization. The Marginal Indians, such as the tall, long-headed bison hunters of the Plains with their rugged bony face, are more like the earliest pre-Mongoloid immigrants. These two stocks—archaic White and Mongoloid—intermingled to form the various types of Amerindians. Birdsell has shown that crosses between Australian aborigines and Mongoloids produce hybrids which could easily be mistaken for American Indians and others resembling Polynesians.

General characteristics of the Amerindians include a yellowish-brown or reddish-brown skin colour; coarse black hair which is usually straight, but in the Indians of the tropical forests is sometimes slightly wavy; very sparse hair on face and body; broad face with prominent cheek-bones; often a well-developed chin. Shovel-shaped incisors are common.

As regards blood groups, the American Indians are remarkable for the absence of B; this suggests that the migrations over the Bering Straits took place before the great increase in frequency of this group occurred in Asia. South and central American tribes have group O almost exclusively. Going northwards, there is a progressive increase in A, which reaches its highest frequency anywhere in the world ($83 \cdot 7\%$) among the Blackfeet. This is accounted for on the basis that A was introduced by later waves of immigrants from Asia. Strikingly uniform frequencies of the MNSs groups and the rhesus series among all Amerindians suggest a common origin too recent to have been affected by selection. Blood-group evidence indicates close relationship between North American Indians and Polynesians; they share a relatively high incidence of M (the rest of Oceania other than Polynesia is characterized by high N) and they also share some of the highest known frequencies of the rhesus gene cDE (Mourant, 1959). Probably this similarity is due to a common 'archaic White' ancestry; but whether it implies trans-Pacific journeys in one direction or another, is still anybody's guess. The Polynesians, however, do not possess the Diego factor, which is characteristic of Amerindians and some other Mongoloids.

Owing to their remarkable homogeneity, classification of the American Indians varies considerably according to different authorities. Reducing the problem to its simplest, two very broad categories may be distinguished: the Marginal Indians who live (or lived) by hunting, fishing and gathering and who, as a whole, are nearer to the archaic White stock; and the agricultural Indians of the southwest and South America who are more Mongoloid in appearance.

North American Indians

In pre-Columbian times, the aboriginal population of North America consisted of hunters, fishermen and food-gatherers except in the South-West, Mexico, and parts of the east and south-east. Nine main cultural areas and peoples are recognized (Fig. 27):

(a) Eskimo Arctic hunters;

(b) Northern hunters of the coniferous forests;

(c) North-west coast fishermen (Alaska to northern California, e.g. Kwakiutl, Salish);

(d) Plateau fishers, hunters and gatherers (Columbia and Fraser river basins);

(e) Intermediate gatherers of roots and seeds (California);

(f) Plains bison hunters;

(g) Eastern and south-eastern chiefdoms of agriculturalists and hunters (e.g. Mohegan, Iroquois, Cherokee, Erie, Choctaw, Seminole);

(h) South-west intensive agriculturalists (Arizona, New Mexico, south-eastern Utah and south-western Colorado);

(i) Mexican and Meso-American agriculturalists (areas of the Toltec, Aztec and Mayan civilizations) (Fig. 28).

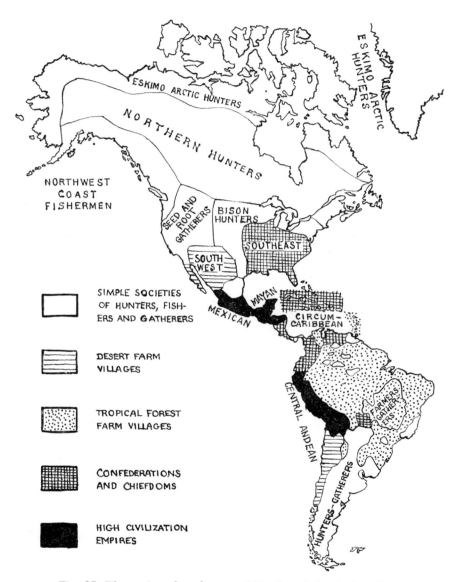

Fig. 27. The main cultural areas of North and South America.

After J. H. Steward, 'Native Peoples of South America' (McGraw-Hill)

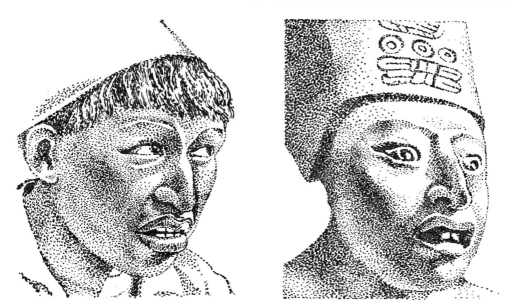

Fig. 28. A Guatemalan Indian who might well have been the model for a Zapotec clay figure from southern Mexico dating from 500–1000 A.D.

After I. Lissner, 'The Living Past' (Cape)

Linguistically, the Indians of North America may be divided into eight main groups, which do not coincide with the cultural areas just mentioned. These groups, with examples of a few of the better-known tribes belonging to each, are as follows:

(*a*) Algonquin (eastern and north-eastern U.S.A.—Blackfeet, Mohegan);

(*b*) Iroquois (eastern U.S.A.—Cherokee, Erie);

(*c*) Caddoan (Plains—Pawnee);

(*d*) Muskhogean (south-eastern U.S.A.—Choctaw, Seminole);

(*e*) Siouan (Minnesota and Plains—Dakota, Crow);

(*f*) Penutian (Plateau—Nez Percé, Chinook);

(*g*) Déné or Athabaskan (Plateau and northern; also south-west—Apache, Navajo);

(*h*) Uto-Aztecan (Meso-America—Aztec, Comanche).

As far as physical appearance is concerned, there are two extreme types—the Plains Indians and the Pueblo of the south-west.

Plains Indians

The tall Plains Indian (see Fig. 26), with long head, prominent cheek-bones and nose (which is not always hooked, as in the popular conception of a Redskin, but may be straight), has many skeletal features similar to the Upper Palaeolithic people of western Europe and the 'old man' of the Upper Cave at Choukoutien. Like the Upper Palaeolithic people, the Plains Indians in former times lived by hunting big game, in this case mainly bison. These comparisons do not imply any relationship between the two, but probably the Plains Indians are near to the archaic White stock, or pre-Mongoloid stock, which was once so widespread and of which the 'old man' of Choukoutien was a representative.

Characteristic of the Plains Indian is a coppery-coloured skin, thin lips, narrow nose with depressed tip, rather receding forehead, strongly developed brow-ridges and prominent chin.

Indians of the South-west

The shorter, stockier Pueblo (including the Hopi) Indians of the South-West are typical Mongoloids. The face is round, the nose short and broad, the skin yellowish-brown. These people and their ancestors have been agriculturalists for thousands of years and may be regarded as the New World equivalents of the Mediterranean race. Archaeological evidence suggests that squash, gourds and beans may have been cultivated in the South-West as early as 5000 B.C. From about A.D. 1 onwards, the history of this area is known in great detail. The Basketmakers (A.D. 1–450) lived in rock shelters, where their remains have been preserved as mummies. They were followed by the Modified Basketmakers (A.D. 450–750) and then by the people of the Developmental Pueblo Period (A.D. 750–1100), a time when hundreds of villages were built (the word 'pueblo' means village). During the Great Pueblo Period (A.D. 1100–1300) the people moved into caves and 'cliff palaces' on account of danger from nomads spreading from the Great Basin. The Basketmaker and Pueblo cultures are now grouped together as the Anasazi culture.

The early Basketmakers were dolichocephalic and the Pueblo people were considered to be brachycephalic until it was recognized that the habit of strapping babies to hard cradle-boards flattened the back of the skull, thus making it broader. It seems that the physical differences between Basketmakers and Pueblos are not at all significant and the cultural evidence shows a continuity of development.

Among the invaders who arrived during the Pueblo period were the Navajo, who differ considerably from the Pueblo Indians in appearance. That they arrived in the South-West not more than a thousand years ago is indicated by the fact that their language, together with that of the Apaches, has no connection with that of neighbouring tribes but belongs to the Athabaskan group spoken by hunters in the north of Canada. In their new environment—the spectacular canyons of the desert—the Navajo became intensive cultivators and expanded enormously; they are now the largest tribe in North America. The Navajo are renowned especially for their blanket weaving and for their elaborate sand paintings.

South American Indians

Four main cultural zones are distinguished in South America:

(a) Circum-Caribbean chiefdoms of agriculturalists and hunters;
(b) Tropical forest agriculturalists;
(c) Central Andean agriculturalists;
(d) Marginal hunters, fishers and gatherers.

(a) The Circum-Caribbean chiefdoms may be compared with those of the south-east of North America. Among the Indians living on the Caribbean shores and islands today, mention must be made of the curious San Blas people who occasioned comments on a 'white race'; in fact they have a most unusual incidence of albinism (about 1%).

(b) The village farmers of Amazonia and eastern Brazil are the counterpart of the Pueblo Indians of the south-western U.S.A., though their environments are entirely different. They are round-headed and, in spite of their tropical habitat, the skin is not dark but yellowish-brown (Fig. 29). This group includes the Jivaro, (Plate VII, left), renowned as head-shrinkers and probably the largest tribe in South America. Most of the Amazon Indians practise a shifting slash-and-burn agriculture, though some live entirely by hunting and food-collecting.

(c) The Central Andean civilizations of Peru, culminating in the Inca empire, were the South American equivalents of the Aztec civilization of Mexico and the Mayan civilization of Yucatan. The ancient inhabitants of Peru are well known from mummies in pre-Inca graves dating from the Chimu period (A.D. 1200–1300). The hair of these mummies sometimes appears reddish, but this is due to the decomposition of melanin. Characteristic of Peruvian and Bolivian skulls is the relatively high frequency of the so-called Inca bone, an island of bone enclosed by branches of the mid-line suture at the back of the skull.

The Incas developed great cities and temples and an elaborate system of roads, but their transport was limited to the back of a llama or alpaca. It was perhaps mainly due to the lack of wheeled transport that the three great pre-Columbian civilizations developed independently and in comparative isolation.

(*d*) The Marginal nomads of the southern part of the continent from Tierra del Fuego to Brazil hunt and collect food in areas too swampy, mountainous, cold or dry for agriculture. The Fuegians include the short Yahgan canoe Indians who collect shellfish on the cold, windswept shores of southern Chile; and the taller

Fig. 29. An Aweti warrior of Brazil, with typically Mongoloid features.

Based on a photograph by A. Cowell, 'The Heart of the Forest' (Gollancz)

Ona of Tierra del Fuego, now almost extinct. The Tehuelche and the Puelche of the pampas and Patagonia live by hunting guanaco with bolas.

Linguistically, the South American Indians are divided into three major groups:

(i) Macro-Chibchan of the northern Andes in Ecuador, Colombia and Central America.

(ii) Andean-Equatorial, stretching from northern Peru southwards through the Andes and the Chilean archipelago to Tierra del Fuego, and east of the Andes into the pampas and Patagonia; this group includes Quechua (the language of the

Incas), Arawakan and Tupian of the equatorial forests, and the languages of the Puelche and Tehuelche hunters. The great cultural variations of the people speaking tongues of this group are explained by the fact that the dispersal of its original speakers took place before agriculture was known in the central Andes, during the 2nd millennium B.C.

(iii) Ge-Pano-Carib, including the languages of the tropical forest agriculturalists as well as those of the hunters and gatherers of the southern headwaters of the Amazon and of the eastern Brazilian highlands and coast.

Physical characters of the South American Indians do not correspond with cultural or linguistic boundaries and can seldom be related with environment. In the southern part of South America, however, the Indians of the western (Chile) coast are short and stocky, while those of the east (Argentine)—where the climate is warmer and drier—are taller and leaner; the tall Ona, for instance, contrast strongly with their neighbours to the west, the short Yahgan. Presumably most of the aboriginal inhabitants of South America, however, arrived too recently and moved about too often for natural selection to have operated to any great extent.

IX

Negroids

Owing to the absence of recognizable fossil Negroid remains before relatively recent times, the question of the origin of this stock is one of the most difficult in the whole racial history of man. The main problems have been the following:

(a) the date of the first appearance of the Negro and the nature of his ancestors;
(b) the relationship between African Negroids and Negrillos (pygmies) and the Oceanic 'Negroids' and Negritos;
(c) the relationship between full-sized Negroids and pygmies;
(d) the origins of the Khoisan people (Bushmen and Hottentots) and their relationship, if any, to Negroes and pygmies.

The first question has already been discussed (p. 47); the answer is that no skeletons with recognizable Negroid traits appear before early post-Pleistocene times in West Africa (Asselar) and the Sudan while in East Africa their occurrence is even later. Skeletons dating from the Pleistocene are either of Caucasoid type (in the east and north) or of a large-skulled Bushmanoid type (in the south).

Regarding the second question, blood-group distributions show no evidence of connections between African and Oceanic 'Negroids', nor between Negrillos and Negritos, though of course it is always possible that a wide divergence in blood-group patterns has taken place during the time the two branches of a hypothetical common stock have been isolated.

The last two problems are even more controversial. Many anthropologists have regarded the little Negrillos and the Bushmen as ancestral to the full-sized Negroids. The minority view, supported in this book, is that both pygmies and Bushmen are reduced survivors of larger peoples and that they have developed their particular characteristics as a result of isolation and selection in special environments.

The Negroid stock is extremely variable, but in general it is characterized by a narrow head, protruding upper jaw (prognathism), rounded forehead, poorly

110

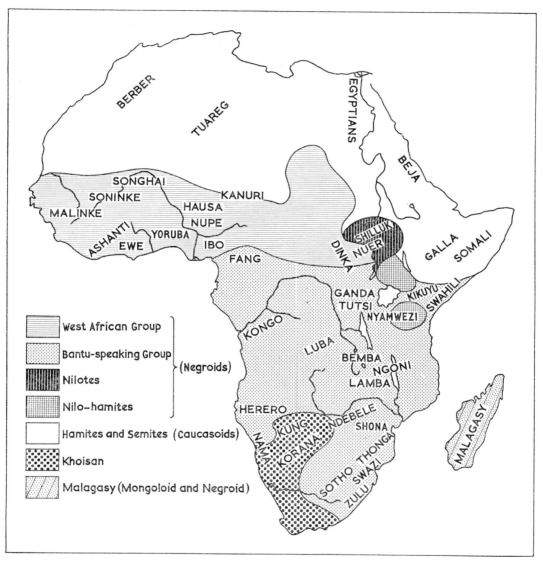

Fig. 30. Simplified distribution map of the peoples of Africa, including names of some of the tribes mentioned in the text.

developed chin, very broad nasal aperture, long, slender forearm and shin, narrow pelvis, very dark skin, woolly hair, sparse beard and body hair, thick, everted lips. The Negro in his most characteristic form is found in West Africa; elsewhere, there has often been admixture with Caucasoids, present early in post-Pleistocene times in East Africa, and reinforced in relatively recent times by the spread of Hamitic-speaking peoples from North Africa and the Horn.

The highly individual blood-group characteristics of the Negroids include the highest frequency of the rhesus combination cDe; the presence of the V gene (part of the rhesus system) in up to 20% of some African populations (whereas its incidence is less than 1% in all other races examined for this gene); the presence of Js, which is independent of all other systems and peculiar to Africans; and the incidence of the Hunter and Henshaw genes, which are very rare outside Africa. The abnormal haemoglobin C is almost entirely restricted to West Africa and the sickle-cell trait is also characteristic of Negroids.

The northern boundary of the Negroids runs from the Senegal river through Timbuktu to Khartoum, thence to the Ethiopian border at 12° N. and so to the Juba river and Indian Ocean (see Fig. 30). Three main races of the Negroid stock may be distinguished: Negro; Negrillo; and Khoisan (some authorities regard the Khoisan people as a separate stock). There are, in addition, three rather distinctive groups of Negroes: the Bantu-speaking Negroids (who in the west are indistinguishable from the West African Negro, but in the east and south probably have small amounts of Caucasoid and Khoisan blood in many cases); the Nilotic Negroids of the headwaters of the Nile and the Lake Victoria region; and the Nilo-Hamites of East Africa who have more Caucasoid admixture than the Nilotes.

1. Negroes

West African Negro

The Negro in his most characteristic form (Fig. 31) lives on the Guinea coast between the Senegal river in the north to the 'Bantu line' on the southern boundary of Nigeria, extending inland as far as the Nile region. The Negroes speak languages of the Niger-Congo and Sudanic groups and it was mainly on linguistic grounds that they were distinguished from Bantu-speakers to the south, though Bantu languages are now regarded as a branch of the Niger-Congo group. For the sake of convenience, however, the Bantu-speakers are described separately although it must be emphasized again that many of them are indistinguishable physically from the West African Negro, whose characters have already been mentioned in connection with the Negroid stock as a whole.

Culturally, too, the West African Negroes and the western Bantu-speakers have much in common, for instance secret societies and wood-carvings to mention only two examples. The artistic talent and technical ability of the West African Negroes reached its highest peak in the superb bronzes, ivories and other sculpture of Ife and Benin (see Fig. 32).

The coastal zone of West Africa, consisting of forests and swamps, is an area of continuous humidity. Its hinterland, apart from the Niger and Benue valleys, becomes progressively more open and merges into steppe country and semi-desert. In this more open country of the Sudan and the southern fringes of the Sahara, trade routes and Moslem influence have been important for the past thousand years and a good deal of admixture between Negroids and Caucasoids has taken place.

In the coastal zone, between the Senegal and Gambia rivers, are the Wolof and Serer, both speakers of the West Atlantic linguistic group. The Wolof, who are said to be the blackest people in Africa, are well built, with broad shoulders and slender waist, often with a fine nose and not strongly everted lips; the Serer have rather coarser features. Stretching inland from the coast to the Upper Niger are the Mande-speakers or Mandingo. They tend to be taller and more slender than neighbouring populations and have finer features and lighter skins. Mande-speakers include the

Fig. 31. A West African Negro, graduate of the University College of Ghana.

Based on a Shell photograph

Soninke, who founded the powerful state of Ghana several centuries before the Arabs arrived in the western Sudan, as well as the Malinke who founded the state of Mali.

The huge Kwa linguistic group includes the Kru-, Nupe-, Akan- and Yoruba-speaking peoples. Some of these were responsible for highly organized states, such as the kingdoms of Yoruba, Ashanti and Dahomey. Renowned for their

H

artistic talent (as well as for their former practice of human sacrifice), the Yoruba of southern Nigeria are among the most progressive peoples of Africa. The Ashanti of Ghana tend to be lighter in build than the Yoruba but, like them, have a long head and very dark skin, wide flat nose and everted lips. The tribes of Dahomey are very varied; they include the Fon, who founded the kingdom of Dahomey early in the 18th century and monopolized trade on the Slave Coast with their formidable army headed by 'Amazons'.

Fig. 32. A Hausa girl with features strikingly similar to those of an ancient terracotta head from Ife.
Hausa girl based on a Shell photograph. Ife head from a photograph, by courtesy of the Editor of 'Man'

The tribes of the hinterland, in the northern territories of Ghana and Nigeria, the eastern parts of the Ivory Coast and French Guinea, the Niger and High Volta regions, are too numerous to be mentioned in any detail. The largest pagan tribe in northern Nigeria is the Tiv. In this vast territory of indigenous pagan tribes, Moslem states such as those of the Fulani and Hausa rose to power.

The Fulani are partly of Berber origin, though they have absorbed varying amounts of Negro blood. The pastoral Fulani have more non-Negroid traits than the sedentary Fulani. The classification of their language, Fufulde, has been most controversial, but is now grouped with the West Atlantic branch of the Niger-Congo family and is related to the languages of the Wolof and Serer. The Fulani conquered the Hausa states during the 19th century. Hausa is a Hamitic language, though racially the Hausa people of northern Nigeria (Fig. 32) are essentially Negroid. They are very dark-skinned, though taller, less prognathous, and with rather narrower nose than most of the Negroes of the west coast.

The Songhai, who live west of the Hausa, along the eastern part of the great bend of the Niger, have mixed a good deal with both the Fulani and the Tuareg. A well-formed nose and coppery-brown skin is characteristic of many of them. Their linguistic stock is independent. The Kanuri of Bornu in north-eastern Nigeria probably also have a good deal of Fulani blood; the Kanembu, another Kanuric tribe further east, have mixed considerably with the Tibu. Bornu-Kanem in the Lake Chad area, and Hausaland further west, became important as terminal points in the trans-Saharan trade routes which developed after the introduction of the camel to North Africa.

On the eastern boundaries of Negroid territory are a large group of Sudanic-speakers, the Azande, who live on the Nile-Congo divide between the Sudan and the former Belgian Congo; the Mangbetu (Plate XII, left) further south are very similar. They are characterized by extreme brachycephaly, very thick lips and rather sloping eyes. The trunk is long in relation to the legs, an unusual feature among the Negroes, and the Azande tend to be rather fat.

Bantu-speaking Negroes

The name 'Bantu' simply means people and this very large group is defined purely on linguistic grounds. The plural prefixes A-, Ba- and Wa- are often attached to tribal names, but they are omitted in this book to avoid confusion (e.g. the people of the kingdom of Buganda are referred to as Ganda rather than Baganda).

The Bantu line (see Fig. 30) starts on the Atlantic coast on the southern boundary of Nigeria, runs across the former French and Belgian Congo to the Lake region, and across Kenya to the mouth of the Juba river on the Indian Ocean. South of this line, the people are nearly all Bantu-speakers with the exception of the Khoisan peoples.

In appearance the Bantu are extremely variable. In general, they are of medium height, often muscular in build, ranging in skin colour from black (for instance the Swazi) to yellowish-brown in the case of tribes who have mixed with Bushmen and Hottentots, such as the Tswana. Usually, however, the skin colour is medium to dark chocolate brown, sometimes with a reddish tint. The head is

long, the face moderately prognathous and the usual characteristics of the Negro
such as everted lips and wide nose are generally present, particularly in the west.
In eastern Africa, admixture with Hamitic-speaking peoples has often been postulated to account for a lower proportion of typically Negroid traits (see Fig. 33).
The old Caucasoid strain which appears in early post-Pleistocene times in East
Africa cannot feature in the make-up of the Bantu-speakers except very indirectly,
for linguistic and other evidence all points to the fact that the Bantu originated in
West Africa and are relatively recent immigrants to the east and south. Oschinsky
(1954) concluded that the Bantu of Uganda represent a racial type intermediate
between the pygmies and the Nilotic Negroids and saw no evidence of admixture
with Hamitic-speaking peoples.

The Bantu of West Africa live north of the Kunene river, extending into
Angola, the South Cameroons and French West Africa and inland over a huge
area of the tropical rain forests of the Congo, as far east as the Lake region. In the
Cameroons and the Gaboon, Bantu-speakers live for the most part in the forest
belt, the Sudanic-speakers in the grasslands and mountain areas. There is little
difference between the two in physical appearance. Bantu tribes in the Congo
include the Kongo and other groups of the Lower Congo and Lower Kasai in the
west; the Mongo and Luba (Plate XII, right) of the Congo basin proper; and
numerous tribes of the Upper Kasai and Katanga in the south.

The eastern Bantu-speakers of Uganda , Rwanda, Burundi, Kenya, Tanganyika,
Malawi and Zambia also form a very numerous group. The Eastern Lacustrine
Bantu comprise the inhabitants of the kingdoms of Uganda, such as the Ganda,
Nkole and Nyoro. Further east, on the western slopes of Mount Elgon, live the
Gisu who speak an archaic Bantu language. The Kikuyu of the Kenya highlands
number over a million and, like the similar Kamba (Fig. 33) to the south-east,
are primarily agriculturalists but also stock-keepers. The Kikuyu began occupying
their present territory over 500 years ago and continued their migrations until
the last century, displacing tribes of indigenous primitive hunters known as the
'Ndorobo.

Between the Kamba and the coast are the Nyika, Pokomo, Giriama, Teita and
other tribes of the thorn-bush country. On the slopes of Kilimanjaro live the
Chagga, relative newcomers to the area, who developed an elaborate system of
agriculture with irrigation and in recent times have achieved a highly successful
coffee-marketing co-operative. Among the other tribes of Tanganyika may be
mentioned the Gogo, Turu and Nyamwezi; in the east are a group called the

Rufiji, which includes the Hehe. An interesting tribe in northern Tanganyika are the Iraqw, whose language is not a Bantu one and is in fact unclassified. Their ancestors may well have been in this part of the country since Stone Age times.

The Swahili of the Kenya and Tanganyika coasts and the islands of Zanzibar and Pemba are much mixed with Arab and Persian blood. They also include in their ancestry slaves from all parts of the country who collected in the great markets of the coast and especially of Zanzibar. Their language, Kiswahili, has become the *lingua franca* of the whole of East Africa.

Fig. 33. A Kamba of Kenya. Many of the eastern Bantu-speaking peoples do not have pronounced Negro characteristics like everted lips and broad nose.

Based on a Shell photograph

In Malawi and Zambia the *lingua franca* changes to Chinyanja. The most important groups are the Maravi (which includes the Nyanja of the Lake Nyasa region); the Makonde (which includes the Ngonde and the Moslemized Yao); and the Ngoni, descendants of the Nguni who fled from Natal early in the 19th century to escape from the Zulu. Ngoni tribes, who live in Malawi, Zambia, Tanganyika and a few in Mozambique, have increased enormously through incorporating conquered peoples and marrying their women. In the Luangwa valley and Bangweulu swamps of Zambia are the Bemba, the largest tribe in the

country; this group includes also the Bisa and Lala. On the Middle Zambezi
are the Lozi peoples of Barotseland. The Barotse nation comprises 25 tribes, of
which the Lozi are the most important; others are the Ila, Tonga and Luba.
Characteristically these people are rather tall, with not very thick lips; the nose
varies from flat and wide to narrow-bridged.

South of the Zambezi and Kunene rivers are the southern Bantu-speakers
of Southern Rhodesia, Mozambique, the Union of South Africa, Bechuanaland,
Basutoland and parts of South West Africa. They number over 14 million people.
The main groups are the Nguni cluster, made up of hundreds of tribes mostly
living between the Drakensberg mountains and the sea; the Shona of Southern
Rhodesia; the Sotho of Basutoland and neighbouring territories; and the Herero
and Ovambo of South West Africa.

Nguni languages, among them Zulu, Xhosa, Swazi and Ndebele, have incor-
porated clicks as a result of Bushman and Hottentot contacts and admixture with
the Khoisan people has also affected the physical appearance of many of the
Nguni. Most renowned of all these people are the Zulu, who had a profound
effect on the distribution and movements of the populations of South Africa.
Starting as a small tribe, they expanded enormously early in the 19th century
under their leader Shaka and conquered most of the inhabitants of Zululand and
Natal. During the resulting chaos, many tribes were wiped out or dispersed, while
those that remained absorbed Zulu culture and language. The Swazi came into
being as a distinct tribe only after Shaka's time. The Ndebele, now living in the
Transvaal and Matabeleland in Southern Rhodesia, have absorbed Sotho culture
and language to a large extent. They founded a powerful state in 1840 and for
many years their raiding parties were the terror of their neighbours. They were
defeated in the Matabele war of 1893, when their leader Lobengula fled. The
Ndebele show much variation in physical characters, having absorbed and mixed
with many of the tribes they conquered. Adjoining the Ndebele are the Shona of
Mashonaland, whose ancestors were associated with many of the ruins of Southern
Rhodesia connected with the ancient gold trade with the Arabs.

The Sotho may be divided into three groups: the southern Sotho of Basutoland;
the western Sotho or Tswana; and the eastern Sotho including the Venda. They
differ with regard to social organization and language from their Nguni and
Thonga neighbours. The Thonga or Shangana-Tonga is a large group of agriculturalists living entirely in Mozambique. Many fled westwards from Shaka's
Zulus and settled in the eastern Transvaal.

The Herero of South West Africa are nomadic cattle-keepers who probably reached Hereroland about the middle of the 18th century. They are tall and slender, with fine features and a rather light-coloured skin. There has certainly been a good deal of admixture with the Hottentots. The agricultural Ovambo claim a close relationship with the Herero; their features are usually more Negroid-looking and their skin colour is often darker.

Nilotes

The Nilotes live in the White Nile region from 200 miles south of Khartoum to Lake Kioga, apart from one group—the Luo—on the eastern shores of Lake Victoria. A northern group includes the Dinka, Nuer and Shilluk; a central group in northern Uganda consists of the Acholi, Lango and Alur; while the Luo live in eastern Uganda and western Kenya.

Most of these people have the broad nose, everted lips and prognathism characteristic of the Negroid, though many have thin nose and lips and a straight profile. Nearly all are strongly dolichocephalic. The Nuer, Shilluk and Dinka are extremely tall, averaging about 178 cm. (5 ft. 11 in.) or more (the Nuer average 180–185 cm.), with particularly long and slender legs. Their typical pose is to stand on one leg, leaning on a spear. The Hamitic element is strongest in the Shilluk, who often have a high-bridged nose and thin lips. The Dinka are purely pastoral, while the Shilluk are agriculturalists as well as herdsmen. In character all these people are noted for their aloofness and disdain for European culture. The Luo and other Nilotic tribes of Uganda such as the Acholi are far more Negroid in appearance than the northern group. The Luo are rather heavily built; they are agriculturalists and the second largest tribe in Kenya after the Kikuyu.

Nilo-Hamites

The Nilo-Hamites (see Plate XI, right), as their name implies, have more of the Hamitic in their make-up than the Nilotes though the term 'Half Hamites', as they are sometimes called, is surely a misnomer. Their territory ranges from the Sudan (the Bari) and Lake Rudolf in Kenya (the Turkana) in the north to about 5° south of the equator in Tanganyika (the Masai). In between are the Teso of Uganda, the Karamojong of eastern Uganda and the Nandi group of western Kenya (including also the Kipsigis, Elgeyo and Suk). The Turkana (Fig. 34) and

Masai are nomadic herdsmen; the Kipsigis and Suk are mainly sedentary, practising agriculture and keeping cattle; while the
others are semi-nomadic.

These people show great variability; many of
them are tall and slender, with long legs, a long
head, often a rather narrow face and non-Negroid
nose (see Plate XI). Some of these tribes were
renowned for their war-like character; the Nandi
and Masai in particular were the terror of Bantu
tribes and early European travellers alike. In spite
of disease—both human and bovine—which has
reduced their numbers enormously in the present
century, and in spite of the fact that many have
taken Kikuyu wives, the Masai have preserved
their identity to a surprising degree. Warriors
with hair in pigtails smeared with red ochre and
fat can still be seen leaning on their spears, quite
indifferent to western civilization. It is often said
that the Masai's way of life is doomed but recent
events have forced the pace of political conscious-
ness among them.

Fig. 34. A Turkana from northern
Kenya (one of the Nilo-Hamitic
tribes: see also Plate XI).

*Based on a photograph in G. W. B. Huntingford
'East African Background' (Longmans Green)*

2. Negrillos or Pygmies

The Pygmies (Plate VIII) are scattered in small groups through the tropical rain
forests within 5° north and south of the equator. They are hunters and food-
gatherers, but are often attached to full-sized Bantu-speaking tribes with whom
they exchange meat for yams, bananas and other agricultural produce. Folklore
and classical tradition suggest that they were formerly more widespread and have
been forced into the forest by pressure from Negroes; early travellers, for instance,
mentioned pygmies in the Ivory Coast and parts of Liberia. The Egyptians por-
trayed pygmies on tombs of the Vth Dynasty (c. 2500 B.C.), yet it is less than a
hundred years since the first European set eyes on these little people (the German
G. A. Schweinfurth in 1870). The pygmies have become amazingly well adapted
to the forest, where their isolation saved them from warfare and slavery. In spite
of admixture with surrounding Bantu-speaking tribes, the pygmy has managed

to keep his individuality; this is probably because he is so well adjusted to his environment. Sometimes, however, hybrid groups are found, such as the Amba of the Fort Portal region who are 6 in. to 1 ft. taller than the true pygmies and show great variability in their features.

These little people are perfectly proportioned and not deformed in any way. The average height of all pygmy groups is around 4 ft. 6 in. to 4 ft. 8 in. Two distinctive types can be distinguished: one very 'infantile' in appearance, round-headed, with a short, broad face, very low-bridged concave nose, narrow shoulders, short legs and almost no beard or body hair; the other type is longer-headed, with longer and narrower face, broader shoulders, well-muscled torso, lighter skin colour, and far more beard and body hair. In general, the skin is reddish, yellowish-brown or very dark brown; the body is often covered with downy hair; the eyes are rather bulging; the face is prognathous; and the arms are very long in comparison with the legs. The hair is sometimes reddish, particularly in children; this is often caused by a disease known as *kwashiorkor* caused by protein deficiency.

Three main groups have been distinguished:

(i) the Eastern group, which includes the Mbuti of the Ituri basin;
(ii) the Central group, including the Twa of the Congo basin;
(iii) the Western group, comprising the Binga of French Equatorial Africa and the Cameroons.

The original language of the pygmies has been lost; the Efe-speaking Mbuti groups of the Ituri forest are the most primitive in a linguistic sense, but even they have borrowed most of their words from surrounding Bantu tribes.

3. Khoisan Peoples

Bushmen and Hottentots

The Bushmen and Hottentots are known collectively as the Khoisan race; this term is made up from the words *Khoi-Khoin* (the Hottentots' name for themselves) and *San* (the Hottentots' name for the Bushmen). Their close relationship is obvious, both from their appearance and from their unique languages distinguished by 'clicks'. It is generally agreed that the Khoisan people extended over a far wider territory in the past—evidence for this includes rock paintings in

H*

Tanganyika very similar to Bushman paintings in South Africa and, even more convincing, is the fact that certain tribes in Tanganyika, the Hadza and the Sandawe, speak languages with clicks. The Hadza are hunters, while the Sandawe are pastoral and agricultural. The Hadza have a very dark skin and do not resemble the Bushmen at all except for the fact that they too sometimes show steatopygia. Blood group evidence shows that there must be a fairly close relationship between the Khoisan peoples and the Negroids. There are, however, certain distinctions, such as the absence of the rhesus negative combination cde in Bushmen and Hottentots, wheras it is relatively frequent in most other African peoples. The frequencies of the haptoglobin gene Hp^1 are significantly lower among Bushmen than among Negroids. There are also a few notable distinctions between Bushmen and Hottentots; while the former have a very low incidence of blood group B, Hottentots have a very high frequency of this gene (which is also high among the Pygmies).

There is little doubt that most of the Khoisan people have been isolated in South Africa for a relatively long time, though only lately have they been confined to the areas of their present distribution: the Bushmen in the central and northern parts of the Kalahari desert, the northern part of South West Africa, and south Angola; the pure Hottentots in South West Africa north of the Orange river. Only a long period of isolation could account for some of their very distinctive characters. Some of the skulls associated with Middle Stone Age industries, dating from the Upper Pleistocene of at least 10,000 years ago, are known as 'Boskopoid'. These skulls are considerably larger than those of the present Bushmen, but have the same pentagoid shape when viewed from above, a characteristic bossing of the sides of the skull towards the back, and a face that is disproportionately small and short. Early Hottentot skulls, on the other hand, are very long and similar to those of the Mesolithic people of East Africa who are of Caucasoid type. The Hottentots may have arisen from a mixture of early Bushmanoid peoples of East Africa with Caucasoids. The divergences between the present Bushmen and Hottentots are almost certainly largely due to Caucasoid admixture in the case of the Hottentots. These differences are apparent also in Hottentot languages (which include certain Hamitic grammatical peculiarities) and in their culture. The cattle and sheep of the Hottentots are similar in breed to those of north-east Africa, introduced by the Hamites. Bartholomew Diaz, the first European to see the Hottentots, mentioned their large herds and flocks. Van Riebeeck distinguished between wealthy classes of Hottentots, with chiefs and tribal organizations, and bands of 'Strandlopers' (beach-combers) who lived mainly on shellfish (these were crosses between Hottentots and Bushwomen).

(i) *Bushmen*

It is clear from the distribution of Bushman skeletal remains and from the Bushman portraits in rock paintings and engravings over the whole of South Africa, that they were formerly far more widespread and were only confined to the inhospitable area of the Kalahari by Bantu tribes, Hottentots and Europeans a few hundred years ago. Only recently have these most interesting Stone Age hunters and food-collectors been studied by anthropologists and it was thought at first that very few remained; within the last few years, however, it was estimated that more than 55,500 Bushmen still survive (though this figure has been disputed). Of the 34 known groups, over half have not yet been studied at all. Linguistically, the Bushmen are divided into three main groups: the southern group, which is almost extinct; the central Kalahari group, whose language differs from those of the other two groups and is similar to that of the Hottentots; and the northern group centred in the north-eastern part of South West Africa. Included in the northern group are the Kung, one of the largest and most independent of the Bushman tribes. Other Kung groups in south Angola call themselves the 'red people'. Each tribe within these three main groups speaks its own dialect and each is made up of hunting bands of up to 100 individuals, who have their own rights over a particular stretch of territory. Their shelters are simple affairs made of branches and they have few possessions. Hunting is done with bow and poisoned arrows, throwing sticks and spears, also by means of traps and pitfalls. The women grub up roots with a pointed digging stick, sometimes weighted with a perforated stone.

Average stature is about 5 ft. 2 in., which is taller than the pygmies; the limbs are slender and the hands and feet small. The skin is yellowish-brown and very wrinkled; the hair is tightly spiralled to form 'peppercorn' tufts separated by bare patches (see Plate IX); the face is flat and small, with prominent cheek-bones, flat nose, pointed chin, bulging forehead with no brow-ridges. The eyes are in narrow slits, often with a medial eye-fold, which probably serves as a protection against sun glare in the desert. The ear is square-shaped, with the rim folded over and the lobe often absent. A fatty accumulation on buttocks and thighs known as steatopygia (Plate X, left) is particularly marked in Bushwomen and is much admired by the men; probably it serves as a reserve store of food and water, particularly needed in pregnancy. The curvature of the lower end of the spine (lumbar lordosis) is exaggerated, which makes the buttocks prominent even when no fat accumulation is present. Young Bushwomen often have very protruberant areolas (see Plate X, right). Certain peculiarities of the genital organs are also characteristic: the penis is often in an almost horizontal position; and in women the extension of the labia minora, forming a 'tablier' or apron, is universal, though whether this character is hereditary or acquired has been disputed.

(ii) *Hottentots*

The Hottentot is very similar to the Bushman, but is slightly taller (average 5 ft. 4 in.) and has a longer, narrower head and more prognathous face. Formerly the Hottentots occupied the whole of the western part of South Africa from the Kunene river in the north to the Cape peninsula, but now there are only scattered remnants north of the Orange river. Linguistically, they were divided into four groups: the Nama, Korana, Eastern Hottentots and Cape Hottentots. The Old Hottentot population of the Cape was largely absorbed by admixture with Dutch colonists and constitutes the basis of the Cape Coloured, Griqua and Rehoboth hybrids. In European/Hottentot crosses, the only characters of the former which predominate are the lighter skin colour and taller stature. The Eastern Hottentots, among whom were the Gonaqua, have also been exterminated or absorbed. The tribal units of the Korana were almost completely destroyed towards the end of the last century through fighting with the neighbouring Basuto and Europeans. The largest group still surviving are the Nama or Namaqua of South West Africa, of whom about 24,000 may be living today. They are pastoralists, keeping long-horned cattle and fat-tailed sheep. Apart from this stock-keeping economy, the Hottentots are also more advanced than the Bushmen in that they smelt iron and make wooden vessels.

The Bergdama of South West Africa are sometimes classed with the Nama Hottentots as they have taken over the Hottentots' language and much of their culture; but racially they are Negroes, although they are very unlike the Bantu-speakers in appearance. They are of small or medium stature, heavily built, with a long head and very dark skin. They live by hunting and food-collecting (in this respect they are similar to the Bushmen rather than the Hottentots.)

References

General

BARNICOT, N. A. 1956. The Pigment Trichosiderin from Human Red Hair. *Nature*, **177:** 528.
—— 1959. Climatic Factors in the Evolution of Human Populations. *Cold Spring Harbor Symposia on Quantitative Biology*, **24:** 115–129.
BIASUTTI, R. 1954. *Le Razze e i Popoli della Terra*. Torino.
BOYD, W. C. 1950. *Genetics and the Races of Man*. Boston.
BROTHWELL, D. R. (edit.). 1963. *Dental Anthropology*. London.
COMAS, J. 1960. *Manual of Physical Anthropology*. Springfield, Ill.
COON, C. S. 1957. What is Race?. *Atlantic Monthly*, **200:** 103–108.
—— 1959. In *Cold Spring Harbor Symposia on Quantitative Biology*, **24:** 153–159.
—— 1963. *The Origin of Races*. London.
COON, C. S., *et al.* 1950. *Races*. Springfield, Ill.
DOBZHANSKY, T. 1955. *Evolution, Genetics and Man*. New York & London
GARN, S. M. 1961. *Human Races*. Springfield, Ill.
HOOTON, A. E. 1947. *Up from the Ape*. New York.
HUIZINGA, J. 1958. Systematic Investigations of the Position of the Greatest Breadth of the Skull. In *Neanderthal Centenary*. Utrecht.
MONTAGU, M. F. A. 1951. *An Introduction to Physical Anthropology*. 2nd edit. Springfield, Ill.
TREVOR, J. C. 1955. Race. *Encycl. Hebraica*. Tel-Aviv.
WEYER, E. 1959. *Primitive People Today*. London.

Blood Groups and other Biochemical Characters

ALLISON, A. C. 1954. Protection afforded by Sickle-cell Trait against Subterian Malarial Infection. *Brit. Med. Journ.*, **1:** 290–294.
GLEMSER, M. S. 1963. Palaeoserology. *In* D. Brothwell and E. Higgs (edits.). *Science in Archaeology*. London.
HARRIS, H., *et al.* 1959. In *C I B A Symposium on Medical Biology and Etruscan Origins*. Ed. by G. E. W. Wolstenholme. London.
HARRISON, G. A. (edit.). 1961. Genetical Variation in Human Populations. *Symposia Soc. Study Human Biol.*, **4.**
HARRISON, G. A., *et al.* 1964. *Human Biology*. Oxford.
KENNEDY, K. A. R. 1964. A Biochemical Analysis of Human Remains from Gua Cha, Kelantan Malaya. *Man*, art. 92.
LEHMANN, F. 1953. The Sickle-cell Trait not an Essentially Negroid Feature. *Man*, **53,** 5.
LEHMANN, F., & RAPER, A. 1949. Distribution of the Sickle-cell Trait in Uganda. *Nature*, **164:** 494–496.
MOURANT, A. E. 1954. *The Distribution of the Human Blood Groups*. Oxford.
MOURANT, A. E., *et al.* 1958. *The ABO Blood Groups*. Oxford.
RACE, R. R., & SANGER, R. 1950. *Blood Groups in Man*. Oxford.
WEINER, J. S. 1959. Blood-group Investigation on Central Kalahari Bushmen. *Nature*, **183:** 843.

CAUCASOIDS

Europe

Bosi, R. 1960. *The Lapps*. London.

Bunak, V. V. 1960. Anthropological Composition of the Population of the Caucasus. *Contributions to the Physical Anthropology of the Soviet Union* (Russian Translation Series, Peabody Museum of Archaeology and Ethnology, Harvard University, **1,** 2).

Charles, R. P. 1960. Le Peuplement de l'Europe Méditerranéenne. *Bull. Soc. d'Anthrop. Paris* (11) **1:** 3–156.

Coon, C. S. 1939. *The Races of Europe*. New York.

Sauter, M. R. 1952. *Les Races de l'Europe*. Paris.

India

Coon, C. S. 1958. Faces of Asia. *University Museum Bulletin Philadelphia*, **22,** 1.

Eickstedt, E. von. 1934. *In* Iyer, A. *The Mysore Tribes and Castes*, **1.**

Fürer-Haimendorf, C. von. 1953. New Aspects of the Dravidian Problem. *Tamil Culture*, **2:** 127–135.

Majumdar, D. N., & Madan, T. N. 1956. *An Introduction to Social Anthropology*. Bombay.

Wheeler, Sir Mortimer. 1959. *Early India and Pakistan*. London.

Africa

Briggs, L. C. 1958. *The Living Races of the Sahara Desert*. Harvard University.

Forde, C. D. 1955–6. North Eastern Africa, Parts I–III. In *Ethnographic Survey of Africa*. International African Institute, London.

AUSTRALOIDS AND PACIFIC ISLANDERS

Abbie, A. A. 1951. The Australian Aborigine. *Oceania*, **22:** 91–100.

—— 1958. The Original Australians. *The Leech*, **28:** 120–130.

Bell, R. E. 1958. New Zealand. *Asian Perspectives*, **2:** 89–95.

Birdsell, J. B. 1949. The Racial Origin of the Extinct Tasmanians. *Rec. Q. Victoria Mus.*, Launceston, **2,** 3: 105–122.

Emory, K. P. 1959. Origin of the Hawaiians. *J. Polynesian Soc.*, **68:** 29–35.

Joesting, E. 1960. The First Hawaiians. *Natural History*, **69:** 37–47.

Keesing, F. M. 1950. Early Migrations in the Southwest Pacific Area. *Southwestern J. Anthrop.*, **6:** 101–109.

Marshall, D. S. 1956. The Settlement of Polynesia. *Sci. American*, **195,** 2: 59–72.

Shapiro, H. L., & Suggs, R. C. 1959. New Dates for Polynesian Prehistory. *Man*, **59,** 3.

Suggs, R. C. 1960. Historical Traditions and Archaeology in Polynesia. *Amer. Anthrop.*, **62:** 764–772.

Tindale, N. B. 1957. Culture Succession in South Eastern Australia. *Rec. S. Australian Mus.*, **13:** 1–46.

MONGOLOIDS

Chang, K. C. 1960. New Light on Early Man in China. *Asian Perspectives*, **2** (1958): 41–61.

Laughlin, W. S. (edit.). 1951. *The Physical Anthropology of the American Indian*. Viking Fund, New York.

STEWARD, J. H., & FARON, L. C. 1959. *Native Peoples of South America*. New York & London.

STEWART, T. D. 1960. A Physical Anthropologist's View of the Peopling of the New World. *Southwestern J. Anthrop.*, **16:** 259–270.

WASHBURN, S. L. 1963. The Study of Race. *Amer. Anthrop.*, **65:** 521–531.

WILLEY, G. R. 1960. New World Prehistory. *Science*, **131:** 73–86.

WORMINGTON, H. M. 1947. Prehistoric Indians of the Southwest. *Colorado Mus. Nat. Hist.*, **7**.

NEGROIDS

FORDE, C. D. (edit.). *Ethnographic Survey of Africa*. International African Institute, London.
1950–57. Western Africa. Parts I–XIV.
1950–60. East Central Africa. Parts I–XI.
1951–53. West Central Africa. Parts I–IV.
1952–55. Southern Africa. Parts I–IV.

HUNTINGFORD, G. W. B., & BELL, C. R. V. 1950. *East African Background*. London.

MURDOCK, G. P. 1959. *Africa*. New York & London.

SCHAPERA, I. 1951. *The Khoisan Peoples of South Africa*. London.

SELIGMAN, C. G. 1957. *Races of Africa*. 3rd. edit. London.

SINGER, R. 1960. Some Biological Aspects of the Bushman. *Z. Morph. Anthrop.*, **51:** 1–6.

TALBOT, P. A. & MULHALL, H. 1962. *The Physical Anthropology of Southern Nigeria*. Cambridge.

TOBIAS, P. V. 1959. Some Developments in South African Physical Anthropology 1938–1958. In Galloway, A. *The Skeletal Remains of Bambandyanalo*. Johannesburg.

WEINER, J. S. 1959. Blood-group Investigations on Central Kalahari Bushmen. *Nature*, **183:** 843.

Index

DATE DUE

SEP 5 72			

GAYLORD

PRINTED IN U.S.A.